The Economic and Environmental Consequences of Nutrient Management in Agriculture

THE ECONOMIC AND ENVIRONMENTAL CONSEQUENCES OF NUTRIENT MANAGEMENT IN AGRICULTURE

WEN-YUAN HUANG AND NOEL D. URI

Nova Science Publishers, Inc.
Commack, New York

Editorial Production: Susan Boriotti
Office Manager: Annette Hellinger
Graphics: Frank Grucci and Jennifer Lucas
Information Editor: Tatiana Shohov
Book Production: Donna Dennis, Patrick Davin, Christine Mathosian, Tammy Sauter and Lynette Van Helden
Circulation: Maryanne Schmidt
Marketing/Sales: Cathy DeGregory

Library of Congress Cataloging-in-Publication Data

Huang, Wen-Yuan.
The Economic and Environmental Consequences of Nutrient Management in Agriculture / Wen-Yuan Huang and Noel D. Uri.
p. cm.
Includes bibliographical references.
ISBN 1-56072-754-3
1. Nitrogen fertilizers. 2. Nitrogen fertilizers--Environmental aspects. I. Uri, Noel D. II. Title.
S651.H826 1999 99-052045
631.8'4--dc21 CIP

227 Main Street, Suite 100
Huntington, New York 11743
Tele. (631)462-6682, (631)424-NOVA Fax (631)462-4666
e-mail: Novascience@earthlink.net
e-mail: Novascil@aol.com
Web Site: http://www.nexusworld.com/nova

Printed in the United States of America

CONTENTS

PREFACE

Nitrogen is an essential plant nutrient required to produce food and fiber. While the increase in the use of nitrogen fertilizer in agricultural production has contributed to the increase in food and fiber production in the United States in recent years, it has also been identified as a major contributor to the elevated concentration levels of nitrates in groundwater and surface water in some regions of the country.

High concentration levels of nitrates in drinking water supplied from groundwater and surface water have become a public concern because of their real and suspected risks to human health. The presence of nitrates in drinking water can cause potentially fatal infant methemoglobinemia (blue baby syndrome). Nitrates are also linked to nitrosamine, a potent carcinogen affecting a wide range of organs in many animal species.

Although nitrates in groundwater and surface water come from various sources, the use of nitrogen fertilizer in agricultural production in the United States has been identified as the major contributor to the presence of nitrates in groundwater and surface water in some states. This conclusion is supported by documented incidents of contamination by nitrogen fertilizer used by farmers in Pennsylvania, Florida, Wisconsin, California, New York, Iowa, and several other states.

Targeting vulnerable areas to reduce nitrate leaching and runoff associated with nitrogen fertilizer use into the groundwater and surface water is a plausible national environmental policy. The targeting approach recognizes the differences in the vulnerability of various types of soils and crops to leaching and runoff and, correspondingly, prescribes different policies to minimize (or at least mitigate) nitrate leaching and runoff. Additionally, targeting is an effective tool if the objective is to maximize net social welfare.

In order to reduce the nitrogen fertilizer use that is a threat to the groundwater under the targeted cropland and surface water adjacent to the targeted cropland, a variety of methods are available. One approach is to adopt a fertilizer-reducing farming practice, such as a crop rotation in which a legume crop (e.g., soybeans) is rotated with a non-legume crop (e.g., corn). The legume crop is used to provide fixed-nitrogen as a substitute for fertilizer-nitrogen. Adoption of this sort of crop rotation can reduce the residual (excess) nitrogen in the soil through a reduction in the frequency and amount of nitrogen fertilizer applied on a field and through the more efficient use of the nitrogen fertilizer applied because of more conducive soil conditions in which to grow a crop.

There are other approaches to addressing the issue as well. The following chapters examine in detail some of these.

Finally, much past research related to water quality problems associated with nitrate contamination has assumed arbitrary levels for reducing the nitrogen fertilizer application rate. Very little has focused on the use of a nitrogen mass balance approach to determine the approximate level to which nitrogen fertilizer application should be reduced. That is, to determine the amount of excess nitrogen available for potential leaching into the groundwater or runoff into the surface water under a farming practice such as a crop rotation, the nitrogen mass balance method must be employed using the nitrogen cycle in order to gain relevant insights into the nature and extent of the problem. This is a critical oversight that will be addressed in several of the subsequent chapters.

A Note on the Authors. Wen-yuan Huang is with the Economic Research Service, U.S. Department of Agriculture. Noel D. Uri is with the Common Carrier Bureau, Federal Communications Commission. The views expressed are those of the authors and do not necessarily represent the policies of the agencies with which they are affiliated.

Chapter 1

THE USE OF FERTILIZER AND ITS ENVIRONMENTAL CONSEQUENCES

INTRODUCTION

Growth in the use of agricultural chemicals has been an integral part of the technological revolution in agriculture. This technological revolution has generated major changes in production practices, shifts in input use, and increases in output and productivity. The mechanization revolution of the 1930s and 1940s has been augmented since 1945 by a biological revolution in terms fertilizer (Carlson and Castle [1972]). That biological revolution continues.

A consequence of these changes is that farmers use more fertilizer but less labor. Indexes of total input use show that labor use (including hired, owner-operator, and unpaid family labor) fell at a 2.9 annual percentage rate between 1948 and 1998 (Ball [1998]).[1] Fertilizer use, on the other hand, increased by 1.6 percent annually.[2] Fertilizer use, however, did not increase at a constant rate over the period 1948-1998. Between 1948 and 1981, for example, fertilizer use increased at an annual rate of 2.6 percent but was approximately unchanged between 1982 and 1998. Agricultural productivity (total output divided by total factor inputs) expanded by 1.9 percent annually over this period (Ball and Nehring [1998], Ball et al. [1998])).

Studies of agricultural chemical productivity report a wide range of economic returns for each dollar spent on fertilizer, but most studies report that the marginal returns of using fertilizer are much greater than the marginal costs. Because fertilizer use often varies simultaneously with the adoption of many other inputs and practices, such as improved seeds, pesticides, mechanization, and tillage practices, the independent

---

1 This index of sectoral labor input accounts for changes in education and the composition of the labor force by incorporating the characteristics of individual workers.

2 As will be discussed below, since the early 1960s the nitrogen content of fertilizer has more than doubled. To account for such a change, a quality difference measured in terms of common attributes have been incorporated into the indexes. These attributes are the various nutrient components of the fertilizer materials.

contribution of fertilizer is difficult to estimate accurately. While most studies report positive marginal returns in the range of $1 to $3 for each dollar spent on fertilizer, for example, some are much higher while others have shown the marginal cost exceeding the return (Headley [1968], Padgitt [1969], Hawkins et al. [1977], Carlson [1977], Duffy and Hanthorn [1978]). More recent studies, however, tend to show lower levels of returns than studies conducted in the 1960s. This decline in the marginal productivity as fertilizer use increased across most agricultural crops is expected. More recent studies would be expected to show a rise in the value of the marginal product if productivity continues to grow, as noted above has been the case since 1982.

While the trends in agricultural chemical use are inherently interesting, a more relevant issue is what underlies the trends. A number of factors have contributed to the changes in the use trends of fertilizer. In the next section, the elements that have precipitated these trends and the changes in the trends will be examined.

FERTILIZER USE TRENDS[3]

From the European settlement of the United States until the 19th century, increased agricultural production came almost entirely from expanding the cropland base and mining the nutrients in the soil. With increased demand for agricultural commodities associated with the increase in the population of the United States, soil nutrient replacement to maintain or expand crop yields were desirable. Manure and other farm refuse were applied to the soils. Later, applications of manure were supplemented with fish, seaweed, peatmoss, leaves, straw, leached ashes, bonemeal, and Peruvian guano, materials that contained a higher percentage of nitrogen, phosphate, and potash than did manure (Wines [1985]). Crop rotations were also used to supply needed nutrients. Early crop rotations included combinations of row crops and small grains with hay and pasture over a 3 to 7 year cycle. Legumes in rotations fix nitrogen from the atmosphere into the soil, and rotations also helped improve soil moisture, control pests and increase yields (National Research Council [1989]). As manufacturing processes developed, production of synthetic chemical fertilizers like superphosphates and later urea and anhydrous ammonia replaced most natural fertilizers produced from recycled wastes. With the introduction of high analysis fertilizers like urea, anhydrous ammonia, and diammonium phosphate, monoculture or continuous same crop plantings for two or more years became popular with crops like corn, wheat, and soybeans.

Commercial fertilizers provide relatively low-cost nutrients needed to fully realize the yield potential of new high-yielding varieties (HYV) of crops (Ibach and Williams [1971]). Since the early 1960s in response to the adoption of the HYV that are nitrogen intensive, U.S. yields per unit of land area for major crops have increased dramatically. Corn yields, for example, increased from 62 bushels per acre in 1964 to 139 bushels in 1994 while wheat yields increased from 26 to 38 bushels during this same time period

---

3 Table 1.1 provides definitions of the primary nutrients supplied by fertilizer.

Table 1.1. Fertilizer Definitions

Nitrogen, phosphorous, and potassium are the primary nutrients supplied by fertilizer.

Nitrogen is a component of amino acids and consequently is critical to protein molecules. It is also part of the chlorophyll molecule. A deficiency can cause chlorosis, a condition of low chlorophyll content. Vigorous plant growth is associated with adequate nitrogen nutrition. One reason is that nitrogen plays a key role in cell division. If cell division is slowed or stopped, so is expansion of the amount of leaf area exposed to the sun. With smaller leaf area the plant loses its potential to produce an adequate yield.

Phosphorous, which is obtained from phosphate, is essential for all living things. It must be present in adequate amounts in living cells before cell division will take place. Phosphorous is always found in abundance in young, fast growing meristematic tissue. Young plants absorb phosphorous rapidly and adequate phosphorous levels provide for extensive root growth and development. The nutrient also has many vital functions in photosynthesis, utilization of both sugar and starches, and in energy transfer processes.

Potassium is obtained from potash and is essential for a variety of processes including photosynthesis rates, fruit formation, winter hardiness, and disease resistance. It is also crucial in translocation of sugars and other products. Through many enzymatic reactions it is also needed for amino acid and protein formation. Plant cells must have adequate potassium to maintain their internal pressure and prevent wilting.

(U.S. Department of Agriculture [1994]). In 1964, the average application rate per fertilized corn acre was 58 pounds of nitrogen, 41 pounds of phosphate, and 35 pounds of potash. By 1994 this rate had increased to 129 pounds of nitrogen, 57 pounds of phosphate, and 80 pounds of potash.

On the input side, changing relative factor prices led to the substitution of fertilizer for other factors because it became relatively less expensive. With the exception of a few years (e.g., 1974 and 1975), the relative change in the price of fertilizer is consistently smaller than the change in the price of other inputs leading to substitution of fertilizer for other factors of production where possible.

Another strong impetus for fertilizer substitution in the decade of the 1970s was the increase in the price of farmland (Hertel et al. [1996]). Between 1970 and the peak year of 1982, per acre farmland values increased from a nominal average of $157 to $715, an increase of 355 percent. Over the same time period, the price of fertilizer increased by slightly more than 195 percent or an annual increase of 5.7 percent. As a consequence farming during this period focused on the intensive margin relying on increased use of fertilizer rather than focusing on the extensive margin by expanding acres planted.

Because the demand for fertilizer is a derived demand, fertilizer use is affected by normal economic influences. A number of economic factors in both the commodity markets and input markets are responsible for the rise in the U.S. consumption of nitrogen, phosphate, and potash from 7.5 million nutrient tons in 1960 to a record high of

23.7 million nutrient tons by 1981, an increase of more than 210 percent (Table 1.2). In the output markets during the 1970s and early 1980s, commodity prices were above their historical average due in part to government price support programs. The average corn price between 1970 and 1979 averaged 80 percent higher than its average a decade earlier.[4] Thus, with farmers equating the value of the marginal product of fertilizer to the price of fertilizer,[5] as the value of the marginal product rose, fertilizer use expanded.

U.S. consumption of nitrogen, phosphate, and potash is also tied to application rates, the share of acreage receiving applications, and total planted crop acreage. As crop acreage increases, fertilizer consumption increases as well. Consequently, government programs that encourage farmers to divert acreage from production can significantly affect fertilizer consumption. Fertilizer use, however, also changes as application rates on specific crops and the proportion of the acreage of those crops fertilized change over time. Thus, for example, the increase in corn production has been a major contributor to the growth in the use of plant nutrients. In 1964 corn accounted for 34 percent of all plant nutrients (including nitrogen fertilizer) used while accounting for 18 percent of planted acreage. By 1998 it was responsible for 49 percent of all plant nutrients used while accounting for approximately 24 percent of total planted acreage.[6] The increase in fertilizer use on corn especially through 1985 was due in part to greater application rates but it was also enhanced by a rise in the proportion of corn acres fertilized with nitrogen and an increase in planted acreage. Application rates for nitrogen and potash were 140 percent greater in 1985 (the peak year for nitrogen fertilizer application until recently) than in 1964, while the rate of phosphate applied rose by 46 percent. During this period, corn planted acreage increased by about 27 percent. Total nutrient use has fallen somewhat from it peak in 1981 along with total crop acreage, particularly in 1983 as a result of the payment-in-kind program which resulted in much idled land. It totaled 22.3 million nutrient tons in 1998. Land values have also dropped from their peak in 1982 ranging from around $550 to $600 per acre in the late 1990s. Commodity prices remained relatively stable from 1980-1998 due to government programs. For example, nominal corn prices averaged $2.38 per bushel between 1980 and 1998 with a standard deviation of 0.45.[7]

Nitrogen, phosphate, and potash all shared in the dramatic increase in nutrient use between 1960 and 1981. The relative use of nitrogen, however, increased much more rapidly. Nitrogen consumption on all crops stood at 2.7 million nutrient tons in 1960, or 36.7 percent of total nutrient consumption. By 1981, nitrogen use had increased to 11.9 million nutrient tons. Nitrogen application rates on corn increased from 58 pounds per

---

4 These are nominal prices. The standard deviations are 0.07 for 1960-1969 and 0.58 for 1970-1979.

5 This is a simple result from neoclassical microeconomic theory.

6 In 1964 total cropland acreage was 292 million acres. In 1994, total acreage was 310 million acres.

7 In this instance, the standard deviation can be used as an indicator of price variability.

Table 1.2. U.S. Commercial Fertilizer Use, 1960-98[1]

		Primary nutrient use			
Year ending June 30[2]	Total fertilizer materials	Nitrogen	Phosphate	Potash	Total[3]
		Million tons			
1960	24.9	2.7	2.6	2.2	7.5
1961	25.6	3.0	2.6	2.2	7.8
1962	26.6	3.4	2.8	2.3	8.4
1963	28.8	3.9	3.1	2.5	9.5
1964	30.7	4.4	3.4	2.7	10.5
1965	31.8	4.6	3.5	2.8	10.9
1966	34.5	5.3	3.9	3.2	12.4
1967	37.1	6.0	4.3	3.6	14.0
1968	38.7	6.8	4.4	3.8	15.0
1969	38.9	6.9	4.7	3.9	15.5
1970	39.6	7.5	4.6	4.0	16.1
1971	41.1	8.1	4.8	4.2	17.2
1972	41.2	8.0	4.9	4.3	17.2
1973	43.3	8.3	5.1	4.6	18.0
1974	47.1	9.2	5.1	5.1	19.3
1975	42.5	8.6	4.5	4.4	17.6
1976	49.2	10.4	5.2	5.2	20.8
1977	51.6	10.6	5.6	5.8	22.1
1978	47.5	10.0	5.1	5.5	20.6
1979	51.5	10.7	5.6	6.2	22.6
1980	52.8	11.4	5.4	6.2	23.1
1981	54.0	11.9	5.4	6.3	23.7
1982	48.7	11.0	4.8	5.6	21.4
1983	41.8	9.1	4.1	4.8	18.1
1984	50.1	11.1	4.9	5.8	21.8
1985	49.1	11.5	4.7	5.6	21.7
1986	44.1	10.4	4.2	5.1	19.7
1987	43.0	10.2	4.0	4.8	19.1
1988	44.5	10.5	4.1	5.0	19.6
1989	44.9	10.6	4.1	4.8	19.6

1990	47.7	11.1	4.3	5.2	20.6
1991	47.3	11.3	4.2	5.0	20.5
1992	48.8	11.4	4.2	5.0	20.7
1993	49.2	11.4	4.4	5.1	20.9
1994	52.3	12.6	4.5	5.3	22.4
1995	50.7	11.7	4.4	5.1	21.3
1996	53.6	12.3	4.5	5.3	22.1
1997	55.0	12.4	4.6	5.4	22.4
1998	55.0	12.3	4.6	5.3	22.3

[1] Includes Puerto Rico. The fertilizer statistics reported include commercial fertilizers purchased for use on farms such as chemical fertilizers and natural processed and dried organic materials. Purchased natural processed and dried organic materials historically have represented about one percent of total nutrient use.

[2] Fertilizer use estimates for 1960-84 are based on U.S. Department of Agriculture [1994 and earlier]. Data for 1985-94 are Tennessee Valley Authority [1995 and earlier] estimates. Those for 1995-1998 come from the Association of American Plant Food Control Officials estimates.

[3] Totals may not add due to rounding.

acre in 1964 to 137 pounds in 1981 and the percent of corn acres receiving nitrogen increased from 85 to 97. Nitrogen use peaked at 12.6 million tons in 1994 and accounted for 56 percent of total nutrient consumption.

Potash consumption follows that of nitrogen, though far behind. Total use of potash increased from 2.2 million nutrient tons in 1960 to 5.3 million nutrient tons in 1995. Potash's share of total primary nutrient consumption has remained relatively stable since the early 1980s.

While nitrogen's share of total plant nutrient consumption increased over this period, phosphate's share declined from 34.5 percent in 1960 to 20.0 percent by 1998. Phosphate use has basically followed a downward trend since 1979. Consumption in 1998 was 4.6 million tons. One primary reason is that plant needs can be met either by direct application of commercial fertilizer or by allowing the crop to utilize residual nutrients already in the soil. Since the late 1970s, U.S. farmers have been taking advantage of residual soil supplies which had been built up on some fields by previous fertilizer and manure applications (National Research Council [1993] and Randall [1994]).

Consequences of Increased Fertilizer Use

An adequate supply of nutrients is essential to crop growth. Ideally, soil nutrients should be available in the proper amounts at the time the plant can use them. Relatively heavy use of nitrogen and some other fertilizers, however, can lead to soil acidification, other changes in soil properties, and offsite environmental problems. Fertilizers are sometimes overapplied. When this occurs, the total amount of plant nutrients available to growing crops not only exceeds the need or ability of the plant to absorb them but exceeds the economic optimum as well. Estimates of crop absorption of applied nitrogen range from 25 to 70 percent and generally vary as a function of plant growth and health and the method and timing of nitrogen application (National Research Council [1989]). Crops are much more likely to utilize fully nitrogen that is properly timed. Unused nitrogen can be immobilized, denitrified, washed into surface water, or leached into groundwater (Huang et al. [1992]).

Proper timing of nitrogen fertilizer avoids supplying an excess that cannot be used by plants thereby becoming a potential source of environmental harm. Since the late 1980s, alternative production practices tied to nutrient mass balance have been emphasized. Best management practices (BMPs) for nutrients have been introduced, including cultural practices such as cultivation, fertilizer use timing, nutrient credits for crop residues and use of manures, precision farming, postharvest management of fields, conservation tillage practices, crop rotations, and the use of biological controls. For example, the value of legumes in fixing nitrogen, improving soil quality, reducing erosion, and increasing yields of subsequent crops are considered. Total fertilizer use and application rates on major crops during the late 1980s and early 1990s have reflected these practices. While their precise impact on fertilizer use is difficult to quantify, the widespread adoption of such cropping practices have served to improve fertilizer use efficiency (Wallingford [1992]).

Still, efforts to provide sufficient nutrition to crops continue to be hindered by inadequate understanding and forecasting of factors that influence nutrient storage, cycling, accessibility, uptake, and use by crops during the growing season. Soil testing can provide the farmer with information to assure adequate nutrition for all agronomic and horticultural crops (Bosch et al. [1995]). But variable soil and climatic conditions that influence nutrient uptake and loss make it difficult to predict the most profitable and environmentally safe levels of nutrient application. Consequently, farmers follow broad guideline that lead to insufficient or excessive fertilization. For example, studies of fertilizer recommendations reveal that some commercial soil testing services consistently recommended the use of far more fertilizer than was needed (Randall and Kelly [1987]). Other studies have suggested that farmers apply fertilizer at rates greater than those required for optimal crop growth as insurance against making a wrong decision that leads to lower yields (Bock and Hergert [1991]).

As alluded to previously, the greatest problem associated with the increase in use of fertilizer in the potential for environmental harm. Water pollution is probably the most damaging and widespread environmental effect of agricultural production. Phipps and Crosson [1986] and Nielsen and Lee [1987] estimate that between 50 and 70 percent of all fertilizer reaching surface waters, principally nitrogen and phosphorous, originate on land in the form of fertilizer. Nitrate moves with water. Thus, nitrogen movement into surface waters more fully reflects the effects of agricultural activity than phosphorous movement does. Phosphorous moves as a passenger bound with sediment, much of which erodes from fields but is not deposited in surface waters (Smith et al. [1987]).

Nutrient loading has had a devastating effect on many lakes, rivers, and bays throughout the United States. Increased nutrient levels stimulate algal growth, which can accelerate the natural process of eutrophication. In its later stages, the algal growth stimulated by nutrients will die and decay, which can significantly deplete available oxygen and reduce higher order aquatic plant and animal populations. The accelerated eutrophication of the Chesapeake Bay is an example of the consequences of nutrient loading from agricultural sources. Nutrient loading in the bay has contributed to a significant decline in the bay fisheries (Kahn and Kemp [1995]).

Nutrient runoff from agricultural land plays a part in estuary degradation. For 78 estuaries examined in 1988, agricultural runoff supplied an average 24 percent of all nutrient loading. In 22 of 78 estuaries, agricultural production contributed more than 25 percent of total nitrogen and phosphorous pollution (U.S. Department of Agriculture [1988]).

THE NEED FOR AN INTEGRATED FERTILIZER USE POLICY

From the foregoing discussion, it is clear that the greatly expanded use of fertilizer has been key in the growth of agricultural productivity in the United States. Additionally, while the increase in the use of fertilizer has been driven by a variety of economic forces, there have been adverse environmental consequences that are not reflected in the economic costs and returns associated with fertilizer use. That is, there are externalities associated with the use of fertilizer.

Externalities exist in situations where the activities of an economic agent affect the preferences, consumption, or technology of another economic agent (Buchanan and Stubblebine [1962]). The presence of externalities is one rationale for government intervention in the production decision process.

As previously noted, externalities play a central role in the economics of the interaction between the agricultural sector and the environment. To mitigate the impact of externalities, a couple of policy options are available to the government. These policy options in general have the potential to affect the production practices adopted by farmers and the use of fertilizer. In what follows, these policy options will be explored.

(a) Regulation

Direct government involvement in the market via regulation is one way that has been advocated to address the externalities arising from the use of fertilizer. Regulation can take a variety of forms ranging from restrictions on the amount of fertilizer that can be applied to outright banning the use of fertilizer because the externality resulting from its use is so egregious. It is generally agreed in the latter case that direct control, or a ban, is the most desirable form of government intervention in the market. That is, when the desired emission level is zero, banning the use of fertilizer is the optimal policy option. A second situation when direct control is best occurs when rapid or temporary variation in pollution levels results as a consequence of, for example, changing weather patterns.

Thus, limiting the application of fertilizer during the spring rainy season could be used to control runoff into surface water and leaching into groundwater (Fisher [1981]).

There are a number of instances in agriculture where a regulatory approach has been suggested as a way of controlling for the externality arising from production. Currently, however, neither the Federal government nor any state government has a comprehensive legal framework for protecting both surface water and groundwater from all agricultural nonpoint source pollution (Ribaudo and Woo [1992]).

One state has a limited regulation governing fertilizer and nutrient use by farmers. Nebraska's Groundwater Management and Protection Act was designed to reduce nitrate concentrations in groundwater by controlling fertilizer use (Williamson [1988]). Increasing concentrations of nitrate in groundwater led to a 1986 law requiring 23 Natural Resource Districts (NRD) covering the state to require best management practices to protect water quality. The practices required depend on nitrate concentration in groundwater. In the least contaminated areas, fall applications of commercial nitrogen fertilizer are prohibited on sandy soil. In Phase II areas (groundwater concentration of nitrates in the range 12.6 to 20 ppm), irrigation wells are to be sampled, irrigation applications metered, deep soil analysis for nitrate performed on every field, fall fertilizer applications banned on sandy soils, and application of nitrogen fertilizer on heavier soils restricted until after November 1. For Phase III, the same restrictions apply as for Phase II. In addition, all fall and winter fertilizer applications are banned and spring applications must be split applications or must use an approved nitrogen inhibitor. Groundwater monitoring in the Central Platte Natural Resources District, which had the greatest problem, has shown a decrease in nitrate concentration in groundwater, suggesting the program is working. Unfortunately, however, no comprehensive economic assessment of the benefits and costs of the Act has, to date, been conducted.

In a limited study of the effects of the Nebraska Groundwater Management and Protection Act, Bosch et al. [1995], found that for Central Nebraska, farmers whose fertilizer applications were subject to direct control were more likely to adopt fertilizer testing. Moreover, the test results were utilized in making nitrogen fertilizer application decisions (ostensibly resulting in lower application rates) compared to farmers outside of the region. In a companion piece, Fuglie and Bosch [1995] find that when uncertainty about the quantity of soil nitrate is highest, the value of soil nitrogen testing is highest, enabling farmers to reduce nitrogen fertilizer use without affecting crop yield.

(b) Tax

The use of a tax is a nonregulatory approach designed to provide incentives to change the behavior of a producer by, for example, applying less fertilizer. As such, a farmer has the choice of whether to adopt a change without fear of legal action. The distinction between a nonregulatory approach and a regulatory approach is important because of the ongoing debate on the degree to which regulatory approaches should be applied to nonpoint source pollution (Baumol and Oates [1988], Fisher [1981], and Johansson [1993]).

Historically, taxes were the first policy instrument proposed to deal with the presence of an externality. Pigou [1932] argued in essence that a farmer when using a polluting agricultural chemical which results in an externality does not bear all of the costs of producing the agricultural commodity. In particular, the marginal private cost of production is less than the marginal social cost of the commodity. This can happen when the property rights are not assigned or transaction costs inhibit negotiation between the farmer and those adversely affected by the use of the fertilizer or pesticide. The difference between the marginal private and social costs is the marginal cost of the externality. When this type of externality occurs, the farmer produces more of the agricultural commodity than is socially optimal. This misallocation of resources (market failure) results in a loss of social welfare. A solution to the problem is to induce the farmer to supply the socially optimal amount of the good by imposing a tax such that the private marginal cost is increased to the point where it just equals the marginal social cost of production (Meade [1952]).

The imposition of a tax on the use of fertilizer has some advantages over other policy approaches dealing with the externalities issue. First, because the use of fertilizer has been shown to respond to market forces, it is efficient to use the market to control the use of fertilizer. Next, because many farmers are involved, the cost of setting and collecting the tax is lower than it is for, say, monitoring nitrate leaching. Additionally, a tax provides an incentive for a farmer to reduce the amount of the input used. If the farmer reduces the use of fertilizer, the associated externalities will coincidentally be reduced. Further, the production of crops not using the fertilizer giving rise to the externalities will be beneficially affected if they are substitutes in production. Their cost of production will be relatively lower and consequently their output will expand relative to the chemical intensive crops. Thus, such production practices as organic farming relying on minimal chemical inputs will be promoted.

Finally, a tax is preferred to other approaches to controlling an externality because it provides a continuing incentive to the polluting farmer to cut back on emissions. No matter how low they are, cutting back further will reduce tax payments. This is especially important in a dynamic setting, where a polluting farmer is encouraged to seek new low-cost ways of reducing pollution through, for example, adopting an alternative production practice that relies less on the polluting input.

One of the drawbacks to using a tax to adjust for externalities is to determine precisely what the optimal tax rate should be. This requires knowledge of what are the marginal social cost and the marginal private cost of production. The determination of these is frequently an iterative process (Baumol and Oates [1988]). The net cost of reducing externalities and hence environmental quality improvement can be represented as a schedule which is a direct function of the tax rate. A given tax rate will be associated with a minimum net cost for a particular level of environmental quality (e.g., amount of nitrate leached). It has been shown that the pollution abatement cost will increase at an increasing rate as environmental quality is improved (Pfeiffer and Whittlesey [1978]).

Using a tax to correct for the externality raises the issue of precisely where to place the tax. In the case of nitrogen which leaches into the groundwater, for example, should the tax be placed on the offending input or should the tax be placed on just the nitrate leached? It has been shown (Holtermann [1976]) that the placement of the tax will affect net farm income with the tax on the actual leaching resulting in the greatest net farm income but the lowest tax revenue. Additionally, placing a tax on one input changes relative factor prices. This results in input substitution that potentially leads to other problems.

Most states tax fertilizer, although most also exempt farmers from such taxes. Farmers must pay the tax only in Iowa, Nebraska, Tennessee, and West Virginia (The Fertilizer Institute [1993]). The tax rates are relatively modest given that the price of, say, anhydrous ammonia fertilizer is currently (circa 1996) about $300 per ton (U.S. Department of Agriculture [April 1996]). Thus, the tax will raise the price of fertilizer to a farmer somewhere between zero (in states that have no fertilizer tax) and $0.10 to $0.75 per ton (in the states where a farmer is not exempt from the fertilizer tax).

What is the potential impact on net farm income and the environment of a fertilizer tax? A number of simulation studies have addressed the question of the effect of higher fertilizer prices due to a tax on agricultural production and the environment. Most are limited in scope, focusing on a narrowly defined geographic area using primarily partial equilibrium models. Additionally, these simulation studies typically do not include any sort of transaction or compliance costs. The extent of the simulated reduction in fertilizer use or loss to the environment depends on (1) the structure of the model being used and (2) the magnitude of the assumed price elasticity of demand for fertilizer.

Garcia and Randall [1994] look solely at the production impacts for U.S. corn and wheat of a ten percent tax on fertilizer using a translogarithmic cost function. They find such a tax reduces fertilizer use by 9.54 percent for corn and 8.76 percent for wheat. This results in corn production in the United States falling by 3.95 percent and wheat production by 2.16 percent. They do not estimate environmental effects.

Quiroga, Fernandez-Cornejo, and Vasavada [1995], using a different methodology, measure the fertilizer tax increase necessary to reduce fertilizer use by 30 percent. They conclude that a tax of 417 percent would be required.

Pfeiffer and Whittlesey [1978] consider a nitrogen fertilizer tax as the approach to abate water pollution in the Yakima Basin of Washington. Farms in the region are typically small and much of the drainage is subsurface during at least part of its return flow to the Yakima River. The target maximum nitrate concentration in the river during August was 0.30 mg/l. The tax required to meet this objective was determined via a linear programming model to be $0.60 per pound. While the fertilizer tax is relatively large (given an assumed fertilizer price of $0.15 per pound), from the standpoint of ease and cost of administration, the authors conclude that such a policy would not be desirable because it could not be administered efficiently by already existing irrigation districts.

Huang and Lantin [1993] use the concept of nitrogen mass balance (which accounts for all nitrogen applied and available for plant uptake and all nitrogen removed after crop harvest) and have as an objective the reduction of excess nitrogen in the soil. Based on a nonlinear mathematical programming model for Iowa field crop production, they suggest that to reduce excess nitrogen to zero (and thus eliminate all nitrate leaching), a tax rate in excess of 200 percent would be needed if crop rotations are used and nearly 500 percent if continuous cropping is used.

Using a linear programming model of cotton production in California, Stevens [1988] finds that a nitrogen fertilizer tax of approximately 100 percent will reduce nitrate loss by about 34 percent while reducing farm profits by about 6.7 percent from the no-tax situation. The assessment, however, does not incorporate risk. It has been shown that risk is an important determinant of farmer behavior (Hazell and Scandizzo [1974], Kramer et al. [1983], and Huang et al. [1993]).

Effects of a tax, like all policy options, vary across the economy. Given that price elasticities for farm chemicals are low, input producers would be able to pass most of the tax along to farmers. To the extent crop supply is diminished, prices would be expected to rise. Consumers would pay higher costs, more likely true for meat and dairy products (from higher feed costs) than for other foods. Taxpayers would benefit from enhanced revenues. Effects on the environment are positive to the extent a tax reduces chemical use and in areas where the specific chemical causes an environmental problem.

Overview

The increase in the use of fertilizer in agricultural production has been associated with a substantial increase in agricultural productivity in the United States. This increase in fertilizer use has been driven by a variety of economic forces including the fluctuation in the price of output and changing relative factor prices. Associated with the increase in the use of fertilizer have been adverse environmental consequences that are not reflected in the costs and returns of agricultural production. That is, externalities exist whose cost need to be internalized. In what follows alternative approaches for dealing with these environmental concerns are explored.

Chapter 2 looks at how a farmer currently growing corn from one year to the next can reduce the excess nitrogen in the soil and increase net farm income in the process by adopting a soybean-corn rotation. Adopting a meadow-corn rotation in deference to planting corn continuously, however, can reduce by a significant amount excess nitrogen in the soil which is available for potential leaching into the groundwater but this will involve a relatively sizeable reduction in net farm income. Additionally, in order to achieve a goal of zero excess nitrogen in the soil over time, both rotation schemes involve a limitation on the nitrogen fertilizer application rate. Practicing the continuous planting of corn while coincidentally limiting the use of nitrogen fertilizer can effectively reduce excess nitrogen in the soil to zero for a relatively low price of nitrogen fertilizer. Adoption of a soybean-corn rotation, however, while simultaneously limiting the nitrogen fertilizer application rate will have the lowest compliance cost for a farmer irrespective of the price of nitrogen fertilizer. Additionally, when the nitrogen fertilizer price is relatively low, a fertilizer use restriction on cropland that is highly vulnerable to potential leaching will have a slightly smaller compliance cost relative to cropland with a moderate leaching potential. This differential declines, however, as the nitrogen fertilizer price increases.

The analysis in Chapter 3 is based on farm-level production decision models for a cotton producer in the United States, if a farmer's perceived probability of not being able to apply nitrogen during the growing season is between zero and one exclusively, then a split application of nitrogen fertilizer is the optimal strategy for both a risk neutral and a risk averse farmer. Additionally, a risk averse farmer will apply more nitrogen fertilizer prior to planting than a risk neutral farmer. Consequently, any policy designed to promote a single application of nitrogen fertilizer during the growing season to minimize nitrogen fertilizer runoff into surface water and to reduce nitrate leaching into groundwater would cause a farmer to move away from his or her optimal nitrogen fertilizer application strategy. This being the case, the farmer would have to have a sufficient incentive to change. This incentive could take a variety of forms.

In Chapter 4 it is shown that for non-irrigated cotton, significantly more nitrogen fertilizer applied during the fall or the spring is lost relative to nitrogen fertilizer applied during the during the growing season. There is no evidence to suggest that the fall application of nitrogen fertilizer incurs a larger loss than that applied in the spring for either non-irrigated or irrigated cotton production. Irrigation practices result in significant nitrogen losses due to increased leaching. Irrigation does, however, reduce nitrogen loss by increasing plant uptake of nitrogen fertilizer. This result is indicated by the fact that the increase in cotton yield associated with irrigation exceeds the yield loss associated with an increase in nitrogen leaching due to irrigation.

Chapter 5 is concerned with costs to a profit-maximizing farmer to comply with a restriction on nitrogen fertilizer use on cropland vulnerable to nitrate leaching. The compliance cost associated varying levels of cropland vulnerability to nitrate leaching are theoretically and empirically investigated using a farm-level dynamic programming model considering the nitrogen carry-over effect. Theoretical result indicates that it is indeterminate whether cropland with a high leaching potential will have smaller or larger compliance cost than cropland with a moderate leaching potential when nitrogen fertilizer use is constrained. An empirical investigation based on an Iowa case study, however, concludes that a fertilizer use restriction on cropland highly vulnerable to leaching will have a smaller compliance cost (i.e., a lower cost to the farmer) per acre and a smaller compliance cost per pound reduction in nitrogen fertilizer application rate relative to cropland with a moderate leaching potential. The per acre cost difference between these two types of cropland is relatively insignificant. The cost per-pound reduction in residual nitrogen, however, can be quite significant. Policy makers interested in determining an equitable financial incentive to compensate a farmer to reduce nitrogen fertilizer use aimed at mitigating a potential nitrate leaching problem should not base their decision on the vulnerability of cropland to leaching. Rather, the decision must be based on an empirical assessment.

Chapter 6 outlines a policy aimed at enhancing water quality in general and reducing nitrate leaching into groundwater in particular. Use of a residual nitrogen tax is an approach to induce farmers to limit nitrogen use. It is a cost-effective way to reduce nitrogen available for potential leaching into groundwater. This policy option forces farmers to implement a nutrient management plan for efficient nitrogen use. This policy tool can be employed to promote sustainable agricultural production systems to utilize nitrogen from legume crops, animal wastes, and crop residues. Since a tax would likely vary by region, a pilot regional study would be needed to assess the effect of a tax on nitrogen use in selected counties and to address problems associated with implementing the tax including predicting farmers' responses to a tax.

The penultimate chapter, Chapter 7, explores the economic benefits to the farmer and the environmental benefits to society associated with soil nitrogen testing (soil N-testing) by a profit-maximizing farmer. These benefits are shown to depend on the farmer's knowledge about nitrogen carry-over as well as current nitrogen management practices. A dynamic fertilizer use decision model is combined with a crop production process model to evaluate the economic and environmental benefits of pre-side-dress soil N-testing for a hypothetical risk-neutral farmer growing corn at the USDAs Agricultural Research Service Sustainable Agriculture Demonstration Farm site in southern Maryland. For the farmer who is knowledgeable about expected nitrogen carry-over, adoption of soil N-testing may lead to a reduction in net farm income but it may also bring about a reduction in nitrogen losses to the environment. For the farmer currently overestimating the expected nitrogen carry-over rate by more than 20 percent, soil N-testing will not lead to a reduction in nitrogen loss but it may lead to an improvement in net farm income. For the farmer currently underestimating the expected nitrogen carry-over rate by more than 25 percent, soil N-testing will help reduce nitrogen losses and lead to an improvement in net farm income. For the farmer who uses a three-year average-yield goal to determine the annual nitrogen fertilizer application rate, use of soil N-testing will help reduce nitrogen loss but it will not result in any improvement in net farm income. Soil N-testing, however, will help the farmer who uses an expected plateau-yield goal improve net farm income and reduce nitrogen loss significantly. While there are differences in the impact on net farm income of the various nutrient management scenarios not relying on soil N-testing relative to the benchmark which is based on soil N-testing, these differences are simply too small to ensure that soil N-testing can lead to an improvement or reduction in net farm income. This is because of the relatively large fluctuations in net farm income attributable to the variability in the weather.

The final chapter, Chapter 8, evaluates the advantage of using insurance to help a farmer adopt a best nutrient management practice (BNMP) that reduces the impact of agricultural production on the environment has been analytically and empirically demonstrated. Using an expected value analysis, it is shown that an insurance program can be structured so as to reduce a farmer's cost of bearing the adoption risk associated with changing production practices and, thus, to improve a farmer's certainty equivalence net farm income thereby promoting the adoption of a BNMP. Using the adoption of growing-season only N fertilizer application in Iowa as a case study, it is demonstrated that insurance may be used to promote the adoption of this practice to reduce N-fertilizer use. It is also shown that it is possible for a farmer and an insurance company both to have an incentive to develop an insurance adoption program that will benefit both the farmer and the insurance company, increasing net social welfare and improving environmental quality in Iowa.

REFERENCES

Ball, E., "Measuring Productivity in Agriculture," *Agricultural Outlook*, Economic Research Service, U.S. Department of Agriculture, Washington, DC, December 1998.

Ball, E., and R. Nehring, "Productivity: Agriculture's Growth Engine," *Agricultural Outlook*, Economic Research Service, U.S. Department of Agriculture, May 1998.

Ball, E., J. Bureau, R. Nehring, and A. Somwaru, "Agricultural Productivity Revisited," *American Journal of Agricultural Economics*, Vol. 79 (1998), pp. 217-231.

Baumol, W. and W. Oates, *The Theory of Environmental Policy*, Cambridge University Press, Cambridge, 1988.

Bock, B., and G. Hergert, "Fertilizer Nitrogen Management," in *Managing Nitrogen for Groundwater Quality and Farm Profitability*, R. Follett and D. Keeney (eds.), Soil Science Society of America, Madison, WI, 1991.

Bosch, D., Z. Cook, and K. Fuglie, "Voluntary Versus Mandatory Policies to Protect Water Quality: Adoption of Nitrogen Testing in Nebraska," *Review of Agricultural Economics*, Vol. 17 (1995), pp. 13-24.

Buchanan, J. and C. Stubblebine, "Externality," *Economica*, Vol. 42 (1962), pp. 371-384.

Carlson, G., "Long-Run Productivity of Inputs," *American Journal of Agricultural Economics*, Vol 59 (1977), pp. 234-241.

Carlson, G., and E. Castle, "Economics of Pest Control," *Pest Control Strategies for the Future*, National Academy of Sciences, Washington, DC, 1972.

Carlson, G., and M. Wetzstein, "Pesticides and Pest Management," in *Agricultural and Environmental Resource Economics*, G. Carlson, D. Zilberman, and J. Miranowski, eds., Oxford University Press, New York, NY, 1993.

Duffy, M., and M. Hanthorn, *Returns to Corn and Soybean Tillage Practices*, AER-508, Economic Research Service, U.S. Department of Agriculture, Washington, DC, 1978.

Fisher, A., *Resource and Environmental Economics*, Cambridge University Press, Cambridge, 1981.

Fuglie, K., and D. Bosch, "Economic and Environmental Implications of Soil Nitrogen Testing: A Switching Regression Analysis," *American Journal of Agricultural Economics*, Vol. 77 (1995), pp. 891-900.

Garcia, R., and A. Randall, "A Cost Function Analysis to Estimate the Effects of Fertilizer Policy on the Supply of Wheat and Corn," *Review of Agricultural Economics*, Vol. 16 (1994), pp. 215-230.

Hawkins, D., W. Slife, and E. Swanson, "Economic Analysis of Herbicide Use in Various Crop Sequences," *Illinois Agricultural Economics*, Vol. 17, No. 1 (1977), pp. 8-13.

Hazell, P. and P. Scandizzo, "Competitive Demand Structures Under Risk in Agricultural Linear Programming Models," *American Journal of Agricultural Economics*, Vol. 56 (1974), pp. 235-244.

Headley, J., "Estimating the Productivity of Agricultural Inputs," *Journal of Farm Economics*, Vol. 50 No. 1 (1968).

Hertel, T., K. Stiegert, and H. Vrooman, "Nitrogen-Land Substitution in Corn Production: A Reconciliation of Aggregate and Firm-Level Evidence," *American Journal of Agricultural Economics*, Vol. 78 (1996), pp. 30-40.

Huang, W., L. Hansen, and N. Uri, "The Effects of the Timing of Nitrogen Fertilizer Application and Irrigation on Yield and Nitrogen Loss in Cotton Production," *Environment and Planning A*, Vol. 24 (1992), pp. 1449-1462.

Huang, W., L. Hansen, and N. Uri, "Nitrogen Fertilizer Timing: A Decision Theoretic Approach for United States Cotton," *Oxford Agrarian Studies*, Vol. 21 (1993), pp. 41-58.

Huang, W., and R. Lantin, "A Comparison of Farmers' Compliance Costs to Reduce Excess Nitrogen Fertilizer Use Under Alternative Policy Options," *Review of Agricultural Economics*, Vol. 15 (1993), pp. 51-62.

Ibach, D. and M. Williams, "Economics of Fertilizer Use," *Fertilizer Technology and Use*, Edited by R. Olson, T. Army, J. Hanway and V. Kilmer, Soil Science Society of America, Madison, WI, 19971.

Johansson, P., *Cost-Benefit Analysis of Environmental Change*, Cambridge University Press, Cambridge, 1993.

Kahn, J., and W. Kemp, "Economic Losses Associated with the Degradation of an Ecosystem: The Case of Submerged Aquatic Vegetation in the Chesapeake Bay," *Journal of Environmental Economics and Management*, Vol. 12 (1995), pp. 246-263.

Kramer, R., W. McSweeny, and R. Stravos, "Soil Conservation with Uncertain Revenue and Input Supplies," *American Journal of Agricultural Economics*, Vol. 65 (1983), pp. 694-702.

Meade, J., "External Economies and Diseconomies in a Competitive System," *Economic Journal*, Vol. 62 (1952), pp. 54-67.

National Research Council, *Alternative Agriculture*, National Academy Press, Washington, DC, 1989.

National Research Council, *Soil and Water Quality*, National Academy Press, Washington, DC, 1993.

Nielson, E., and L. Lee, *The Magnitude and Costs of Groundwater Contamination from Agricultural Chemicals*, Economic Research Service, U.S. Department of Agriculture, Washington, DC, 1987.

Padgitt, M., *Resource Productivity in the Corn Belt, 1964*, Masters thesis, University of Missouri, 1969.

Pfeiffer, G., and N. Whittlesey, "Controlling Nonpoint Externalities with Input Restrictions in an Irrigated River Basin," *Water Resources Research*, Vol. 14 (1978), pp. 1387-1403.

Phipps, T., and P. Crosson, *Agriculture and the Environment*, The National Center for Food and Agricultural Policy, Washington, DC, 1986.

Pigou, A., *The Economics of Welfare*, 4th edition, Macmillan Publishing Company, London, 1932.

Quiroga, R., J. Fernandez-Cornejo, and U. Vasavada, "The Economic Consequences of Reduced Fertilizer Use: A Virtual Pricing Approach," *Applied Economics*, Vol. 27 (1995), pp. 211-217.

Randall, G., "Role of Crop Nutrition Technology in Meeting Future Needs," in *Future Agricultural Technology and Resource Conservation*, B. English, J. Maetzold, B. Holding and E. Heady (eds.), Iowa State University Press, Ames, IA, 1994.

Randall, G., and P. Kelly, *Soil Test Comparison Study*, Agricultural Experiment Station, University of Minnesota, St. Paul, MN, 1987.

Ribaudo, M., and D. Woo, "Summary of State Water Quality Laws Affecting Agriculture," *Agricultural Resources: Cropland, Water, and Conservation*, Economic Research Service, U.S. Department of Agriculture, Washington, DC, September 1992.

Smith, R., R. Alexander, and M. Wolman, "Water Quality Trends in the Nation's Rivers," *Science*, Vol. 235 (1987), pp. 1607-1615.

Stevens, B., "Fiscal Implications of Effluent Charges and Input Taxes," *Journal of Environmental Economics and Management*, Vol. 15 (1988), pp. 285-296.

Tennessee Valley Authority, *Commercial Fertilizers*, Economic and Marketing Staff, Oak Ridge Tennessee, 1995 and earlier.

U.S. Department of Agriculture, "Agricultural Chemicals and the Environment," *Agricultural Outlook*, Economic Research Service, U.S. Department of Agriculture, Washington, DC, 1988.

U.S. Department of Agriculture, *Crop Production*, Economic Research Service, U.S. Department of Agriculture, Washington, DC, 1995 and earlier.

Wallingford, G., "Cotton Fertilizer Efficiency - A Closer Look," *Farm Chemicals*, Vol. 155 (January 1992), pp. 58-60.

Williamson, D., "Implementation of the Nebraska Nitrate Control Legislation," *Nonpoint Pollution: 1988 - Policy, Economy, Management and Appropriate Technology*, American Water Resources Association, November 1988, pp. 133-39.

Wines, R., *Fertilizer in America: From Waste Recycling to Resource Exploitation*, Temple University Press, Philadelphia, PA, 1985.

Chapter 2

THE IMPACT OF FARMING PRACTICES ON REDUCING EXCESS NITROGEN FERTILIZER USE

INTRODUCTION

Targeting vulnerable areas to reduce nitrate leaching associated with nitrogen fertilizer use into the groundwater is a plausible national environmental policy. The targeting approach recognizes the differences in the vulnerability of various types of soils to leaching and, correspondingly, prescribes different policies to minimize (or at least mitigate) nitrate leaching. Additionally, the targeting approach is an effective tool if the objective is to minimize the social cost of the program (Tietenberg [1978] and Baumol and Oates [1988]).

In order to reduce the use of nitrogen fertilizer on targeted cropland, a variety of methods are available. One approach is to adopt a fertilizer-reducing farming practice, such as crop rotation in which a legume crop (e.g., soybeans) is rotated with a non-legume crop (e.g., corn). The legume crop is used to provide fixed-nitrogen as a substitute for fertilizer-nitrogen. Adoption of this sort of crop rotation can reduce the residual (excess) nitrogen in the soil through a reduction in the frequency and amount of nitrogen fertilizer applications on a field and through the more efficient use of the nitrogen fertilizer applied because of more conducive soil conditions in which to grow a crop. The benefits and costs associated with this approach are the focus of this chapter.

This chapter uses as the basis of its analysis the farm-level cost of adopting alternative farming practices aimed at reducing the excess application of nitrogen. The excess application of nitrogen is defined as the difference between the amount of nitrogen applied and the amount of nitrogen in both plants and crops harvested and removed from the field at the end of the growing season. The analysis focuses on crop rotations for corn production because corn uses large amounts of nitrogen fertilizer. Moreover, the continuous growing of corn (i.e., growing corn from one planting season to the next) is targeted for change because it is a common farming practice accounting for approximately one quarter of the corn acres planted in the United States. The continuous planting of corn uses nitrogen fertilizer inefficiently and is potentially a substantial source of nitrate leaching into the groundwater.

In what follows the concept of excess nitrogen will be discussed. Next, various options designed to reduce the excess application rate of nitrogen fertilizer, which leads to the presence of excess nitrogen available for potential leaching into the groundwater, will be delineated and their cost to a farmer indicated. Finally, a case study will be used to estimate the relative costs to a farmer of reducing excess nitrogen fertilizer application.

THE DEFINITION OF EXCESS NITROGEN

To determine the amount of excess nitrogen available for potential leaching into the groundwater under a farming practice such as a crop rotation pattern, the nitrogen mass balance method is employed using the nitrogen cycle (Bundy [1988] and Gilliam and Hoyt [1987]). The amount of excess nitrogen, n_e, available for potential leaching associated with farming activities is defined as the difference between the amount of nitrogen applied from all sources on one acre of cropland and the amount of nitrogen present in both plants and crops harvested and removed at the end of the growing season, n_p. The amount of nitrogen applied includes that from nitrogen fertilizer, n_f, nitrogen credited from previous legume crops, n_s, and nitrogen from manure application, n_m. The excess nitrogen available for potential leaching over a continuous time interval, t, is thus computed as

$$(2.1) \quad n_e(t) = n_f(t) + n_s(t) + n_m(t) - n_p(t)$$

Note that this definition is concerned with excess nitrogen caused only by human farming activities.[1] It assumes that, for a given acre, the amount of nitrogen available for plant uptake from atmospheric nitrogen absorbed by the soil and nitrogen from the organic matter in the soil are negligible after subtracting nitrogen losses attributable to other factors. These other factors include nitrogen losses due to denitrification, volatilization, water run-off, and soil erosion. It also assumes that the excess nitrogen leaves the field at the end of each growing season. Finally, it assumes a long-run, steady state of the nitrogen residue level in the soil. Any of the assumptions above can be removed and a different estimate of excess nitrogen can be calculated. For instance, for a particular cropland site encountering significant soil erosion, the nitrogen loss due to soil erosion can be estimated and subtracted from the right-hand-side of equation (2.1).

---

1 An accurate estimate of the excess nitrogen available for leaching is obviously very difficult to obtain. The problem is associated with the difficulties in distinguishing between leaching and denitrification and with delineating between nitrogen losses and changes in the organic nitrogen level in the soil. The reader interested in pursuing this issue can find a good discussion in Blackmer [1987].

As defined, the concept of excess nitrogen has considerable practical appeal. Using the indicated definition, a farmer is able to estimate the amount of nitrogen added and the amount of nitrogen removed from a field to calculate the excess nitrogen residual in the soil. A farmer using this relationship can efficiently apply nitrogen fertilizer to minimize the excess application of nitrogen. A farmer can also use it to approximate the amount of nitrogen available for potential leaching in areas where soil conditions favor water infiltration. In these areas reducing excess nitrogen that is available for potential leaching is tantamount to reducing excess nitrogen leaching into the groundwater.

OPTIONS TO REDUCE NITROGEN FERTILIZER USE

As noted above, rotating crops is one way a farmer can reduce his or her application of nitrogen fertilizer. This is what will be considered here. Several crop rotations will be evaluated to provide information on the relative costs of adopting alternative farming practices designed to reduce the nitrogen fertilizer application rate. The cost to a farmer of the rotations considered will vary from one option to another. The farm-level performance of various crop rotations under four different options is considered.

(a) No Restriction

Under this option, cropland which employs a crop rotation pattern to reduce the nitrogen fertilizer application rate is currently (or is eligible to be) in the existing farm program in the United States. This option is used as the basis for comparison of the different crop rotation patterns. No nitrogen credits are considered for growing legume crops prior to planting corn and no fertilizer use restrictions are imposed on a farmer. Two types of cropland are considered under this option - cropland with a high potential for leaching and cropland with a moderate leaching potential.

(b) Continuous Planting of Corn with a Restriction on Nitrogen Fertilizer Use

A farmer continuously planting corn under this option will be allowed to participate in the existing United States farm program but he or she is required to reduce the nitrogen fertilizer application rate to the point where there is zero excess nitrogen available for potential leaching as defined by equation (2.1).

(c) Soybean-Corn Rotation with a Restriction on Nitrogen Fertilizer Use

A farmer growing soybeans and corn in rotation will be allowed to participate in the existing United States farm program under this option but he or she will be required to reduce the nitrogen fertilizer application rate so that the excess nitrogen available for potential leaching as defined by equation (2.1) is equal to zero. There will be a credit for nitrogen fixed by soybeans.

(d) Meadow-Corn Rotation with a Restriction on Nitrogen Fertilizer Use

Under this option a farmer growing meadow and corn in rotation will be allowed to participate in the existing United States farm program but he or she will be required to reduce the nitrogen fertilizer application rate so that the excess nitrogen available for potential leaching as defined by equation (2.1) will equal zero. Note that there will be a credit for nitrogen fixed by meadow.

DETERMINING THE NITROGEN FERTILIZER APPLICATION RATE

Different options can have different impacts on a farmer's decision with regard to the application rate of nitrogen fertilizer. An unconstrained, profit-maximizing farmer will equate the value of the increased output associated with using one additional pound of nitrogen fertilizer to the cost of that additional pound of nitrogen fertilizer to determine the optimal nitrogen fertilizer application rate for a particular crop rotation. Thus, for example, under the existing United States farm program and no nitrogen fertilizer use restriction, a farmer would apply fertilizer up to the point where value of the marginal product associated with the application of nitrogen fertilizer equals the nitrogen fertilizer price. Participation in the existing program involves a lump-sum payment to a farmer regardless of his or her nitrogen fertilizer application rate.

In order to formalize the farmer's decision process, consider the following. For an initial level of nitrogen in the soil, n_0, a farmer is confronted with selecting a crop rotation subject to several constraints and physical relationships. Assume that the farmer is confronted with a set of viable crop rotations, $\{r_n, n=1, 2, ..., N\}$, and has as his or her objective the maximization of net per acre return, Z, which is accomplished by choosing the optimal crop rotation, r*. The decision process is therefore defined by

$$(2.2) \quad Z(n_0, r^*) = \text{Maximize } \{z(n_0, r_n), n=1, 2, ..., N\}$$

where

$$(2.3) \quad Z(n_0, r_n) = \int_r ((p^{i(rn)}(t)\, y^{i(rn)}(t) - w\, n_f^{i(rn)}(t) - c^{i(rn)}(t))(1+s)^{-1})dt$$

where $p^i(t)$ is the market price of crop i at time t, $y^i(t)$ is the per acre yield of crop i harvested at time t, w is the price of nitrogen fertilizer, $n_f(t)$ is the nitrogen fertilizer application rate at time t, $c^i(t)$ is the per acre production cost excluding the cost of nitrogen fertilizer at time t, and s is the rate of discount.[2] Note that the $i(r_n)$ indicates that a specific crop is grown at each time period but that this crop might change depending on the rotation being considered over the integral.

2 The discount rate is assumed to equal 0.04 throughout the analysis. See Dervis et al. [1982] for a discussion of the reasonableness of this value.

This decision process will be subject to a series of constraints and physical relationships exclusive of any constraints imposed in order to limit nitrogen fertilizer use. These include

(a) The amount of nitrogen available for plant uptake, n_a, is limited by the per acre nitrogen fertilizer application rate, n_f, and the residual nitrogen available from the previous periods for use at time t, n_r:

(2.4a) $n_a(t) = n_f(t) + n_r(t)$.

(b) The residual nitrogen at time t, $n_r(t)$, is a function of the excess nitrogen available for potential leaching, $n_e(t)$, and the residual nitrogen carried over from the previous period, $n_r(t-1)$:

(2.4b) $n_r(t) = f(n_e(t), n_r(t-1))$

where $n_e(t)$ is defined in equation (2.1).

(c) There is an initial amount of residual nitrogen in the soil:
(2.4c) $n_r(0) = n_0$.

(d) Nitrogen uptake by crop i at time t, $n_p(t)$, is a linear function of the crop yield:

(2.4d) $n_p(t) = a\, y^i(t)$

where a is a constant and the other terms are as previously defined. For the analysis here, it is assumed that a=0.9. That is, there is 0.9 pounds of nitrogen contained in one bushel of corn (Fertilizer Institute [1976]).

(e) Crop yield at time t, $y^i(t)$, is assumed to be a function of the nitrogen available for plant uptake at time t, $n_a(t)$:

(2.4e) $y^i(t) = g^i(n_a(t))$.

Finally, it is assumed that no manure is applied by the farmer. That is, throughout the subsequent analysis, it is assumed that $n_m = 0$

In order to empirically implement the model specified, it is necessary to have explicit representations for two sets of functions - the residual nitrogen transformation functions, $n_r(t) = f(n_e(t), n_r(t-1))$, and the crop yield functions, $y^i(t) = g^i(n_a(t))$. These will be discussed next.

FUNCTIONAL REPRESENTATIONS

(a) Residual Nitrogen Transformation Functions - The Continuous Planting of Corn

The amount of residual nitrogen in the soil, $n_r(t)$, under the continuous planting of corn at time t is given as

(2.5) $n_r(t) + n_\ell(t-1) = n_a(t-1) - n_p(t-1) + n_i(t-1)$

where $n_R(t)$ is the amount of nitrogen leached at time t and $n_i(t)$ is the inherent nitrogen from precipitation at time t. If the excess nitrogen available for potential leaching is greater than zero, it is assumed that k (for k between zero and 1) of it is leached. That is,

(2.6) $n_\ell(t) = k\, n_e(t)$

$= k\,(n_a(t) - n_p(t)).$

Given this equation, relationship (2.5) can be rewritten as

(2.7) $n_r(t) = (1-k)\,(n_a(t-1) - n_p(t-1)) + n_i(t-1).$

A precise determination of a value for k is difficult to make. The value can be approximated, however, using the procedure suggested by Schaffer et al. [1990].[3] In areas where the groundwater is extremely vulnerable to nitrogen contamination due to leaching, the value of k will approach 1 while for areas where leaching is very unlikely, the value of k approaches 0. In the subsequent analysis, a value of k=1 will be used for areas considered to have a high potential for leaching while a value of k=0.5 will be used for areas where the leaching potential is only moderate.

---

3 Schaffer et al. [1990] suggest the use of the following relationship in order to determine an appropriate value for k:
$k(t) = (1 - \exp(-1.2\, wal(t))/por$
where wal(t) is the water available for leaching at time t and por is the porosity of the soil in the root zone. The variable wal(t) is computed as
$wal(t) = pe(t) - et(t) - (awhc - wr(t))$
where pe(t) is the effective precipitation at time t, et(t) is the potential evapotransipiration at time t, awhc is the water holding capacity of the soil, and wr(t) is the water content of the soil at time t. In implementing relationship (2.7), an average value for k(t) across time periods is assumed.

(b) Residual Nitrogen Transformation Functions: The Legume - Corn Rotation

The amount of residual nitrogen in the soil at time t when a legume crop (either soybeans or meadow) is grown is given as

$$(2.8) \quad n_r(t) + n_\ell(t\text{-}1) = n_s(t\text{-}1) + n_a(t\text{-}1) - n_p(t\text{-}1) + n_i(t\text{-}1)$$

where $n_s(t)$ is the legume-fixed nitrogen that can be used for growing corn and the other terms are as previously defined.

If it is further assumed that there is no nitrogen leaching when legume crops are grown, then there is no fertilizer applied to the legume crops and there is no plant uptake of nitrogen. Note that these assumptions are consistent with those made by Schaffer et al. [1990]. Given these assumptions, the relationship defining the residual nitrogen in the soil is

$$(2.9) \quad n_r(t) = n_s(t\text{-}1) + n_i(t\text{-}1).$$

(c) Yield Functions

Before discussing the yield functions, it is necessary to comment on the data used in the estimation since the data define the nature of these functions. The yield data relating yield and nitrogen fertilizer use were obtained from an Iowa State University research study (Iowa State University Experiment Station [1989]). This study examined the impact of nitrogen fertilizer application rates and crop rotation patterns on crop yields. In the study only the nitrogen fertilizer application rate and the sequence of crop rotations varied. All other factors were held constant. These data are used to estimate the yield functions for specific crop rotations. Estimated yield functions are used as the basis of the analysis. The crop rotations considered are soybean-corn (BC) and meadow-corn (MC) in addition to the continuous planting of corn. These rotations are common in the Corn Belt region of the United States (Daberkow and Gill [1989]). The nitrogen fertilizer application rate for corn production varies between rotations. In each rotation only corn production receives nitrogen fertilizer.

The estimated yield functions for the three different crop sequences are given in Table 2.1. The coefficient estimates were obtained via ordinary least squares. Tests for common econometric problems including heteroscedasticity, functional misspecification, and multicollinearity did not reveal any deficiencies. The intercept term on the yield function for the continuous planting of corn is used as the measure of the inherent productivity of the soil. The intercept is the annual corn yield that would be realized from the soil without the application of any nitrogen fertilizer. The difference between the intercepts on the yield functions when corn is continuously planted and when one of the legume-corn crop rotation sequences is planted is the yield response attributable to the nitrogen fixed by the legume crop which is used subsequently by the corn. Finally, the intercept of the yield function for the continuously planting corn is used to compute the initial nitrogen level, n_0, in the soil.

Table 2.1. Estimated Coefficients for Yield Response to Nitrogen Fertilizer Application Rates for Different Preceding Crops[1]

Rotations	A(i,j)	B(i,j)	C(i,j)	R^2
Corn after	65.64	0.730	-0.0017	0.94
Corn	(4.31)	(0.088)	(0.0004)	
			Sample size = 16	
Corn after	107.0	0.521	-0.0012	0.94
Soybeans	(5.1)	(0.105)	(0.0004)	
			Sample Size = 8	
Corn after	149.9	0.165	-0.0004	0.79
Meadow	(3.17)	(0.066)	(0.0003)	
			Sample Size = 8	

[1] The yield function is specified as y(i,j) = A(i,j) + B(i,j)(n_a(i,j)) + C(i,j)((n_a(i,j))**2 where y(i,n) denotes the yield for crop i preceded by crop j, n_a(i,j) is the nitrogen fertilizer application rate for crop i when preceded by crop j, and A(i,j), B(i,j) and C(i,j) are coefficients to be estimated. In the field experiments, only corn received nitrogen fertilizer applications.

Note that the values in parentheses are standard errors of the estimates.

POLICY OPTIONS

As noted above the options that are considered are those designed to limit the use of nitrogen fertilizer. The objective is to reduce excess nitrogen available for potential leaching to zero. This requires introducing two additional constraints into the problem formulation. The first additional constraint requires that the residual nitrogen carried over from one period to the next, $n_r(t)$, plus the nitrogen fertilizer applied, n_f, must be less than or equal to the nitrogen removed from the field through plant uptake and removal of the harvested crop. That is,

$$(2.10) \quad n_r(t) + n_f(t) \leq 0.9\, y^i(t).$$

The second constraint requires that the nitrogen fixed by a legume crop, $n_s(t)$, plus the inherent nitrogen, $n_i(t)$, plus the nitrogen fertilizer applied, $n_f(t)$, must be less than or equal to the nitrogen removed from the field. That is,

$$(2.11) \quad n_s(t) + n_i(t) + n_f(t) \leq 0.9\, y^i(t).$$

Finally, before turning to a discussion of the results, a brief description of the origin of the rest of the data used in implementing the model is required. Cost of production data are from Duffy and Chase [1988]. The cost data represent average production costs for farms in Iowa (Iowa State University [1989]). The commodity price data are from the Economic Research Service [1990]. The December 1989 nitrogen fertilizer price ($0.15 per pound) is assumed to prevail initially although a sensitivity analysis is included in order to examine the effect that variations in the price of nitrogen fertilizer have on the results.

EMPIRICAL RESULTS

Excess nitrogen fertilizer application rates, corn yields, and net farm incomes under the crop planting sequences previously discussed are computed. Each crop planting sequence is assumed to have a six year horizon. It is further assumed that there is no nitrogen fertilizer "carry over" between plantings if the cropland has a high leaching potential and that there is no nitrogen credits from legumes if corn is continuously planted. Subsequently, restricting the use of nitrogen fertilizer while simultaneously accounting for the nitrogen fixed by the legume crop will be assessed. Finally, the costs to a farmer of operating under a restricted fertilizer use environment will be evaluated. The Generalized Algebraic Modeling System (GAMS) is used to solve the farm-level decision model (Kendrick and Meeraus [1985]).

(a) No Fertilizer Use Restrictions

Switching from the continuous planting of corn to one of the crop rotations while imposing no fertilizer use restrictions will reduce the nitrogen fertilizer application rate and excess nitrogen while increasing net farm income. Table 2.2 shows these values if it is assumed that the existing farm program is in effect. The soybean-corn rotation has the highest net farm income over a six year period ($789), while the meadow-corn rotation has the lowest ($655). This is not surprising since growing meadow precludes production of a marketable crop. The continuous planting of corn has the highest per acre nitrogen fertilizer application rate (193 pounds per acre) but the lowest per acre corn yield (143 bushels per acre), while the meadow-corn rotation has the lowest per acre nitrogen fertilizer application rate (116 pounds per acre) but the highest per acre corn yield (164 bushels per acre).

A relatively large amount of nitrogen from the application of nitrogen fertilizer is required in order to receive the highest net farm income. Nitrogen fixed by a legume crop alone will not be sufficient to produce corn. Consequently, the largest net farm income will be realized only if nitrogen fertilizer is applied by the farmer. This result is contingent on the relatively low ratio of the price of fertilizer to the price of corn ($0.15/$2.10=0.071). The per acre difference in the nitrogen fertilizer application rate between the continuous planting of corn and the soybean-corn rotation is small (7 pounds). The meadow-corn rotation needs an additional 116 pounds of nitrogen fertilizer per acre to grow corn efficiently in addition to the nitrogen fixed by the meadow. If the nitrogen applied in the form of fertilizer and that fixed by the legume crop are considered in concert, both the soybean-corn and meadow-corn rotations exhibit excess nitrogen available for potential leaching on cropland susceptible to high (i.e., k=1) as well as moderate (i.e., k=0.5) leaching.

Table 2.2. Nitrogen Fertilizer Application Rate, Corn Yield, Excessive Nitrogen, and Net Farm Income with No Fertilizer Use Restriction

Crop Rotation	Nitrogen Fertilizer Application Rate	Corn Yields	Excessive Nitrogen	Net Farm Income
Continuous Planting of Corn				
- High Potential for Leaching	193	143	384	760
- Moderate Potential for Leaching	170	143	124	781
Soybean-Corn				
- High Potential for Leaching	186	162	237	789
- Moderate Potential for Leaching	186	162	118	789
Soybean-Meadow				
- High Potential for Leaching	116	164	133	655
- Moderate Potential for Leaching	116	164	67	655

Note that the nitrogen fertilizer application rate is in pounds per acre per year, corn yields are in bushels per acre per year, excessive nitrogen is in pounds per acre over a six year time period, and net farm income is in dollars per acre over a six year time period.

(b) Limiting Nitrogen Fertilizer Use

Next, consider the impact on a farmer when nitrogen fertilizer use is constrained as defined by relationships (2.10) and (2.11). While the price of corn is assumed to be $2.10 per bushel (as before), it is now assumed that the price of nitrogen fertilizer ranges between $0.05 and $0.45 per pound in $0.10 increments. (This assumption allows for a study of the sensitivity of the results to fluctuations in the price of nitrogen fertilizer.) Each planting pattern is examined based on one of two types of cropland. These types correspond to their leaching potential. For cropland with a high potential for leaching, it is assumed that for each time period, t, any unused nitrogen will be lost and hence cannot be used for future (i.e., t+1, t+2, ...) crop production. For cropland with a moderate leaching potential, it is assumed that 50 percent (i.e., k=0.5) of the residual nitrogen is carried over from one period to the next. Given these assumptions, in evaluating the yield response functions, $n_a(t)$ will equal $n_f(t)$ for cropland with a high potential for leaching while $n_a(t)$ will equal $n_f(t)$ plus $n_r(t)$ for cropland with a moderate leaching potential. The amount of nitrogen fixed by legumes is estimated, as previously indicated, by the difference between the intercept terms on the various yield functions.

The effect on fertilizer application rates and net farm income of limiting nitrogen fertilizer use are shown in Table 2.3a and Table 2.3b, respectively. The bottom line is that in order to have zero excess nitrogen available for potential leaching, a significant reduction in the nitrogen fertilizer application rate is required for each of the planting options considered (i.e., the continuous planting of corn, a soybean-corn rotation, and a meadow-corn rotation). Although both soybeans and meadow fix nitrogen that is available for the subsequent production of corn, the nitrogen fertilizer application rate for both the soybean-corn and the meadow-corn rotations is constrained (i.e., constraint (2.11) is binding). This result is a consequence of the relatively low price of nitrogen fertilizer (at $0.15 per pound). A higher nitrogen fertilizer price at $0.35 will impact the fertilizer application rate on just the meadow-corn rotation. Utilizing the residual nitrogen in the soil, $n_r(t)$, will reduce the excess nitrogen available for potential leaching at the same time resulting in an increase in net farm income. This reduction in excess nitrogen and gain in net farm income, however, are mitigated as the price of nitrogen fertilizer increases. Further, under the limiting nitrogen fertilizer use option, the soybean-corn rotation will have the largest effect on net income. It becomes the most profitable practice if the nitrogen fertilizer price rises above $0.35 per pound.

(c) Compliance Cost

Finally, a farmer is inherently concerned with the effect on net farm income of adopting a different cropping practice. This effect can be computed simply as the difference in net farm income from the continuous planting of corn assuming that this is the practice initially employed by the farmer and that the planting occurs under a soybean-corn or meadow-corn rotation. It is nominally referred to as the compliance cost. The compliance costs for the three different crop planting schemes were computed assuming that a farmer was planting his or her crops, first, on land with a high potential for leaching and, second, on land with a moderate potential for leaching. The results are presented in Table 2.3a. They show that when the nitrogen fertilizer price is relatively low, a fertilizer use restriction on cropland that is highly vulnerable to potential leaching will have a slightly smaller compliance cost relative to cropland with a moderate leaching potential. The compliance cost on both types of cropland decreases as the price of nitrogen fertilizer price increases. The soybean-corn rotation with a restriction on fertilizer use has the lowest compliance cost. In fact, this compliance cost becomes negative such that the net farm income under the soybean-corn rotation actually exceeds the net farm income from the continuous planting of corn for a price of nitrogen fertilizer exceeding $0.25 per pound.

Table 2.3a. Nitrogen Fertilizer Application Rate When Nitrogen Fertilizer Use is Constrained

Crop Rotation	Nitrogen Fertilizer Price $0.05	$0.15	$0.25	$0.35	$0.45
Continuous Planting of Corn with No Fertilizer Use Restriction					
- On Cropland with a High Potential for Leaching	207	193	180	165	151
- On Cropland with a Moderate Potential for Leaching	170	166	162	157	146
Continuous Planting of Corn with a Restriction on Fertilizer Use	114	114	114	114	114
Soybean- Corn Rotation with a Restriction on Fertilizer Use	93	93	93	93	93
Meadow- Corn Rotation with a Restriction on Fertilizer Use	67	67	57	0	0

Note that the nitrogen fertilizer prices are in dollars per pound and the nitrogen fertilizer application rates are in pounds per acre per year.

Table 2.3b. Net Farm Income When Nitrogen Fertilizer Use is Constrained

	Nitrogen Fertilizer Price				
	$0.05	$0.15	$0.25	$0.35	$0.45
Crop Rotation Continuous Planting of Corn with No Fertilizer Use Restriction					
- On Cropland with a High Potential for Leaching	855	760	672	590	515
- On Cropland with a Moderate Potential for Leaching	864	781	689	617	540
Continuous Planting of Corn with a Restriction on Fertilizer Use	707	653	599	545	492
Soybean-Corn Rotation with a Restriction on Fertilizer Use	759	738	716	694	673
Meadow-Corn Rotation with a Restriction on Fertilizer Use	665	650	635	628	628

Note that the nitrogen fertilizer prices are in dollars per pound and the net farm incomes are in dollars per acre over a 6 year horizon.

Associated with each of the cropping patterns discussed will be a change in nitrogen fertilizer use. These changes will impact net farm income. The effect on net farm income of a change in nitrogen fertilizer use for each option is given in Table 2.3b. The reduction in net farm income associated with the change in nitrogen fertilizer use when the cropland is highly vulnerable to potential leaching relative to cropland with a moderate leaching potential is quite significant. For example, at a nitrogen fertilizer price of $0.15 per pound, the fall in net farm income when excess nitrogen is reduced by one pound under the soybean-corn rotation in areas with a moderate potential for leaching is nearly twice that as in areas with a high potential for leaching. Given that analogous results hold over most of the range in the price of nitrogen fertilizer considered, it can be concluded that reducing excess nitrogen in soils with a moderate leaching potential results is a greater decline in net farm income than would be realized if the soil possesses a high potential for leaching when the nitrogen fertilizer price is between $0.15 and $0.35.

CONCLUSIONS

For a farmer currently growing corn from one year to the next, adopting a soybean-corn rotation can reduce the excess nitrogen in the soil and increase net farm income in the process. Adopting a meadow-corn rotation in deference to continuously planting corn, however, can reduce by a significant amount excess nitrogen in the soil which is available for potential leaching into the groundwater but this will involve a relatively sizeable reduction in net farm income. Additionally, in order to achieve a goal of zero excess nitrogen in the soil over time, both rotation schemes involve a limitation on the nitrogen fertilizer application rate.

Practicing the continuous planting of corn while coincidentally limiting the use of nitrogen fertilizer can effectively reduce excess nitrogen in the soil to zero for a relatively low price of nitrogen fertilizer. Adoption of a soybean-corn rotation, however, while simultaneously limiting the nitrogen fertilizer application rate will have the lowest compliance cost for a farmer irrespective of the price of nitrogen fertilizer.

Additionally, when the nitrogen fertilizer price is relatively low, a fertilizer use restriction on cropland that is highly vulnerable to potential leaching will have a slightly smaller compliance cost relative to cropland with a moderate leaching potential. This differential declines, however, as the nitrogen fertilizer price increases.

Finally, what are the general implications of these results for the selection of a policy to reduce excess nitrogen available for potential leaching into groundwater? First, any of the options considered will impose some costs on a farmer in terms of higher costs of production and/or lower net farm income. This is at odds with the United States farm program in general which seeks to bolster net farm income. A reconciliation of these objectives is clearly needed. Second, any program directed at reducing excess nitrogen available for potential leaching will be applied to all farmers uniformly. This historically has been the nature of such programs. They are not discriminatory in that they do not target one group of farmers at the expense of or to the benefit of others. Given this, the program will impose greater costs on some farmers relative to others because some cropland is more vulnerable to leaching that other cropland. Moreover, if the difference in vulnerability is as severe as Nielsen and Lee [1987] indicate that it is between some regions, the inequity can be quite sizeable.

One final caveat is in order. The foregoing analysis has been based on a number of simplifying assumptions incorporated into a partial equilibrium model. Thus, the model developed looks only at corn which was produced with a given technology as specified by the yield function. But any policy restricting the use of nitrogen fertilizer will not only impact the production of corn but will affect the production of other field crops as well. This is not included in the analysis. These and similar concerns must temper unequivocal acceptance of the results. The conclusions serve as a guide to policy but they are not absolute.

REFERENCES

Baumol, W. and W. Oates, *The Theory of Environmental Policy*, 2nd edition, Cambridge University Press, Cambridge, 1988.

Blackmer, A., "Losses and Transport of Nitrogen From Soil," Chapter 5 in *Rural Groundwater Contamination*, edited by F. D'Itri and L. Wolfson, Lewis Publishers Inc., Chelsea, MI, 1987.

Bundy, L., "The Development of a Nitrogen Management Model: Potential for Site-Specific Groundwater Protection," *Agricultural Chemicals and Groundwater Protection: Emerging Management and Policy Options*, Proceeding of a Conference Held at St. Paul, MN, October 22-23, 1988.

Cantor, P., "Health Effects of Agrichemicals in Groundwater: What Do We Know?" *Agricultural Chemicals and Groundwater Protection: Emerging Management and Policy*, Proceedings of a Conference held at St. Paul, MN, October 22-23, 1988.

Daberkow, S. and M. Gill, "Common Crop Rotations Among Major Field Crops," in *Agricultural Resources: Inputs Situation and Outlook Report*, AR-15, Economic Research Service U.S. Department of Agriculture, Washington, DC, August 1989.

Dervis, K., J. De Melo, and S. Robinson, *General Equilibrium Models for Policy Development*, Cambridge University Press, Cambridge, 1982.

Duffy, M., and C. Chase, "Impacts of the 1985 Food Security Act on Crop Rotations and Fertilizer Use," unpublished manuscript, Department of Agricultural Economics, Iowa State University, Ames, IA, 1988.

Economic Research Service, *Agricultural Outlook*, AO-165, U.S. Department of Agriculture, Washington, DC, p. 52-53, September 1990.

Freshwater Foundation, *Nitrates and Groundwater: A Public Health Concern*, The Freshwater Foundation's Health and Environment Network, Navarre, MN, 1988.

Fertilizer Institute, *The Fertilizer Handbook*, 2nd edition, The Fertilizer Institute, Washington, DC, 1976.

Gilliam, J. and G. Hoyt, "Effect of Conservation Tillage on the Fate and Transport of Nitrogen," in *Effects of Conservation Tillage on Groundwater Quality: Nitrates and Pesticides*, edited by C. Logan, Lewis Publishers, Chelsea, MI, 1987.

Glaser, L., *Provisions of the Food Security Act of 1985*, AIB No. 498, Economic Research Service, U.S. Department of Agriculture, Washington, DC, 1986.

Iowa State University Experiment Station at Kanawha, *Experiment Station Report ORC87-14,22*, Iowa State University, Ames, IA, 1986.

Iowa State University, *Estimated Costs of Crop Production -1989*, Extension Publication, FM-1712, Iowa State University, Ames, IA, December 1989.

Kendrick, D., and A. Meeraus, *GAMS: An Introduction*, Development Research Department, World Bank, Washington, DC, 1985.

Nielsen, E. and L. Lee, *The Magnitude and Costs of Groundwater Contamination From Agricultural Chemicals: A National Perspective*, AER-576, Economic Research Service, U.S. Department of Agriculture, Washington, DC, October 1987.

Office of Technology Assessment, *Protecting the Nation's Groundwater From Contamination*, U.S. Government Printing Office, Washington, DC, 1984.

Pollack, S., and L. Lynch, *Provisions of the Food, Agriculture, and Trade Act of 1990*, AIB-624, Economic Research Service, U.S. Department of Agriculture, Washington, DC, June 1991.

Schaffer, M., A. Halvorsen, and F. Pierce, "Nitrate Leaching and Economic Analysis Package (NELP): Model Description and Application," in R. Follett (ed.), *Managing Nitrogen for Groundwater Quality and Farm Profitability*, Soil Science Society of America, Madison, WI, 1990.

Tietenberg T., "Spatially Differentiated Air Pollutant Emission Charges: An Economic and Legal Analysis," *Land Economics*, Vol 54. (1978), pp. 265-77.

U.S. Environmental Protection Agency, *National Statistical Assessment of Rural Water Conditions*, U.S. Environmental Protection Agency, Washington, DC, June 1984.

Chapter 3

THE APPLICATION TIMING OF NITROGEN FERTILIZER

INTRODUCTION

A farmer can minimize this excess nitrogen emitted into the environment through a variety of production practices. For example, applying nitrogen fertilizer during the times when plant uptake is greatest and when the potential for nitrogen losses due to soil erosion, rainfall, and other environmental factors are minimized will mitigate nitrogen losses. Thus, the application of nitrogen fertilizer after planting in some areas can be more effective than the pre-planting application in reducing nitrogen losses (Bock [1984] and Kanwar et al. [1988]).

Why then would a farmer apply nitrogen prior to planting if applying nitrogen fertilizer after planting can reduce nitrogen losses and, therefore, costs? The objective of the following analysis is to evaluate the factors that affect a farmer's decision concerning the timing of nitrogen fertilizer application and, in turn, answer this question. The key elements considered are the expected nitrogen loss associated with application timing, seasonal variations in nitrogen fertilizer application costs (including the nitrogen fertilizer price and operating costs),[1,2] and a farmer's perceived risk of being unable to apply nitrogen after planting because of weather and field conditions.

In assessing the issue, behavioral models are employed using the analytical framework of Feinerman et al. [1990] to explain why most farmers might practice the split application of nitrogen fertilizer whereby some nitrogen fertilizer is applied before planting and some after planting. Results of the 1989 Cotton Water Quality Survey conducted by the U.S. Department of Agriculture are used to verify the integrity of the behavioral model considered. The data reflect farming practices with regard to the use

---

1. Nitrogen fertilizer prices are, in general, lower in the fall than in the spring. For example, from 1995 to 1999, the spring price of anhydrous ammonia was, on average, 10 percent higher than the fall price of the preceding year (National Agricultural Statistics Service [1999]).
2. Operating costs include such things as hired labor costs, energy expenses to operate farm machinery, etc.

and timing of nitrogen fertilizer application in the production of cotton in the United States.

This chapter is organized into four sections. In the first section, two different farm-level decision models for production are formulated that include factors that affect a farmer's decision concerning the timing of nitrogen fertilizer application. The models differ based on the assumed risk preference of a farmer. In the second section, the 1989 Cotton Water Quality Survey data are used to estimate nitrogen fertilizer losses due to timing of application and irrigation. These estimates are combined with the farm-level production decision models in the third section to determine an optimal timing for nitrogen fertilizer application to explain the timing decisions of the cotton farmers in the United States. The final section offers the conclusions.

A Farm-Level Decision Model of Production

In this section a farm-level decision model for production will be developed in order to examine the factors affecting decision concerning the timing nitrogen fertilizer applied for both irrigated and dryland (non-irrigated) cotton production.[3] Consider the cotton production function

(3.1) $Y(N_a, W| V)$

where N_a is the nitrogen fertilizer available during the growing season, W is the irrigation rate and V is a vector of site specific variables (including such things as the slope of the cropland, soil permeability, and soil organic matter content). It is assumed that $MY/MN_a \$ 0$ and $\partial^2Y/\partial^2N_a \leq 0$. Both N_a and W are a farmer's decision variables while V represents the characteristics of the cropland over which a farmer has little control.[4] The variable N_a is defined as[5]

(3.2) $N_a = N_f (d_1 - e_1) + N_s (d_2 - e_2) + N_g (1 - e_3)$

---

3 Both irrigated and dryland cotton production are considered coincidentally in order to fully utilize the 1989 Cotton Water Quality Survey data. The survey questionnaire makes a distinction between the two different production practices.

4 Obviously, the irrigation rate will equal zero in both the fall and spring. To keep the notation as simplified as possible, however, the form of the production will not be changed between periods.

5 An alternative specification for N_a was considered where

$$N_a = N_f (d_1 - e_1 W) + Ns (d_2 - e_2 W) + Ng(1 - e_3 W)$$

where the e_is (i=1,2,3) represent nitrogen losses associated with irrigation and the other terms are as defined in the text. None of the e_is, however, were statistically significantly different than zero at the 5% level in preliminary analyses. Consequently, this specification is not used in the exposition.

where N_f is the amount of nitrogen fertilizer applied in the fall, N_s is the amount of nitrogen fertilizer applied in the spring, and N_g is the amount of nitrogen fertilizer applied during the growing season. The parameters d_1 and d_2 represent the portions of the nitrogen fertilizer applied in the fall and spring, respectively, that are available for plant uptake during the growing season. The parameters, e_1, e_2, and e_3 represent, respectively, the portions of fall, spring, and growing season nitrogen fertilizer losses associated with irrigation. Thus, e_1, e_2, and e_3 are zero when there is no irrigation. Faced with an expected cotton price of p_c, water costs for irrigation of r_w, and fall, spring, and expected growing season nitrogen fertilizer prices of r_f, r_s, and r_g, respectively, and imputed operating costs of OC,[6] a farmer will endeavor to maximize his or her expected utility of net farm income, p, given as

$$(3.3)\qquad Z = E\,[U(p)] = E\,[U(p_c\, Y(N_a, W|\, V) - r_f\, N_f - r_s\, N_s - r_g\, N_g - r_w\, W - OC)]$$

where E is the expectation operator and U(p) is a monotonically increasing and concave von Neumann-Morgenstern utility function where $\partial U(p)/\partial p > 0$ and $\partial^2 U(p)/\partial^2 p \leq 0$ (Anderson et al. [1977]).

Next, assume that P represents a farmer's perceived probability of having weather and field conditions that prohibit nitrogen fertilizer from being applied after planting. A risk neutral farmer maximizes his or her expected utility of net farm income by maximizing expected profit (Arrow [1971] and Borch [1968]).[7] Consequently, the objective function for a risk neutral farmer becomes

$$(3.4)\qquad \begin{aligned} Z = {} & (p_c\, Y(N_a, W|\, V) - r_f\, N_f - r_s\, N_s - r_g\, N_g - r_w\, W - OC)\,(1\text{-}P) \\ & + (p_c\, Y(N_a, W|\, V, N_g{=}0) - r_f\, N_f - r_s\, N_s - r_w\, W - OC)\, P \end{aligned}$$

where $Y(N_a, W|V, N_g{=}0)$ is the yield function when N_a includes no growing season nitrogen fertilizer application.[8]

The first order conditions for the optimal levels of N_f, N_s, N_g and W that maximize Z are

$$\partial Z/\partial N_f = \qquad p_c\,(d_1 - e_1)(\partial Y(N_a, W|\, V)/\partial N_a$$

---

6 Imputed operating costs are defined as the computed marginal labor, energy and machinery costs for each unit of irrigation water and nitrogen fertilizer applied. Operating costs vary with the fertilizer application method. For example, the cost of applying fertilizer will be less when the fertilizer is applied coincidentally with cultivation (or irrigation) than when it is applied separately (Taylor [1991]).

7 A risk neutral farmer will not change his or her behavior in response to a variation in profit. That is, for a risk neutral farmer, $\partial^2 U(\pi)/\partial^2 \pi = 0$ (Deaton and Muellbauer [1980]).

8 Note that there is an implicit assumption here that the prices of the factors of production remain unchanged between the two scenarios. Assuming they are different, which they might or might not be depending on a variety of economic considerations, needlessly complicates the analysis.

$$- (\partial Y(N_a, W| V)/\partial N_a - \partial Y(N_a, W| V, N_g{=}0)/\partial N_a) P)$$
$$- r_f \le 0$$

(3.5) $$\partial Z/\partial N_s = p_c (d_2 - e_2)[\partial Y(N_a, W| V)/\partial N_a$$
$$- (\partial Y(N_a, W| V)/\partial N_a - \partial Y(N_a, W| V, N_g{=}0)/\partial N_a) P]$$
$$-r_s \le 0$$
$$\partial Z/\partial N_g = (p_c (1 - e_3)\, \partial Y(N_a, W| V)/\partial N_a - r_g)(1 - P) \le 0$$
$$\partial Z/\partial W = p_c\, \partial Y(N_a, W| V)/\partial W\, (1 - P)$$
$$+ (\partial Y(N_a, W| V, N_g{=}0)/\partial W - r_w) P \le 0.$$

Note that the term $(\partial Y(N_a, W| V)/\partial N_a - \partial Y(N_a, W| V, N_g{=}0)/\partial N_a)P$ found in the first and second relationships is the expected (marginal) productivity gains due to a split application of nitrogen fertilizer.

From these first order conditions, the optimal timing of nitrogen fertilizer application can be determined (1) when growing-season application is not possible (i.e., $P = 1$), (2) when growing-season application is not restricted (i.e., $P = 0$), and (3) when growing-season application may be possible (i.e., $0 < P < 1$). These are considered in turn.

(a) Nitrogen Fertilizer Application When Growing-Season Application Is Not Possible

When the growing-season application of nitrogen fertilizer is not possible, $N_g = 0$ and $P = 1$. Thus, the first order conditions relating to nitrogen fertilizer application from the relationships given in (3.5) can be written as

$$p_c (d_1 - e_1) (\partial Y(N_a, W| V, N_g{=}0)/\partial N_a) \le r_f$$

(3.5a) $$p_c (d_2 - e_2) (\partial Y(N_a, W| V, N_g{=}0)/\partial N_a) \le r_s.$$

Solving these two relationships will give an optimal nitrogen fertilizer application rate either for the fall or the spring, or for an optimal fall/spring split application. Moreover, these relationships will give the necessary condition for preferring a fall application over a spring application. This is given by[9]

(3.6) $$(d_1 - e_1)/(d_2 - e_2) \ge r_f/r_s.$$

Spring application is preferable to a fall application if the converse relationship holds. Note that the relationship given in (3.6) holds even if P is not equal to 1. The selection of either a fall or a spring application is not affected by the value of P. Proof of this statement is straightforward and hence left to the reader.

9 Using the first order conditions in (3.5a), fall nitrogen fertilizer application is preferable to spring application if the adjusted fall nitrogen fertilizer cost is less than the adjusted spring fertilizer cost, assuming all other things equal. That is, fall application is preferred if
$r_f/(d_1 - e_1) \le r_s/(d_2 - e_2)$.
This relationship can be rewritten as
$(d_1 - e_1)/(d_2 - e_2) \ge r_f/r_s$.

(b) Nitrogen Fertilizer Application When Growing-Season Application Is Not Restricted

When growing season application of nitrogen fertilizer is not restricted (i.e., $P = 0$), the first order conditions of (3.5) relating to nitrogen fertilizer application can be written as

$$\begin{aligned} &p_c\,(d_1 - e_1)(\partial Y(N_a, W|\,V)/\partial N_a) \le r_f \\ (3.5b)\qquad &p_c\,(d_2 - e_2)(\partial Y(N_a, W|\,V)/\partial N_a) \le r_s \\ &p_c\,(1 - e_3)(\partial Y(N_a, W|\,V)/\partial N_a) \le r_g. \end{aligned}$$

The solution to this system of relationships gives an optimal application rate for nitrogen fertilizer for the fall, the spring, or the growing-season. It can be shown[10] that fall application is preferred to growing season application when

$$(3.7)\qquad (d_1 - c_1)/(1 - c_3) \ge r_f/r_g$$

and that spring application is preferred to growing season application when

$$(3.8)\qquad (d_2 - e_2)/(1 - e_3) \ge r_s/r_g.$$

If the goal is to promote growing season nitrogen fertilizer application,[11] then relationships (3.7) and (3.8) can be used to determine a tax on nitrogen fertilizer to be applied in the fall or spring to discourage a farmer from applying fertilizer before planting. Alternatively, the relationships can be used to determine a subsidy to nitrogen fertilizer applied during the growing season to provide a farmer with an incentive not to apply nitrogen fertilizer before planting. Thus, for example, a tax on nitrogen fertilizer applied in the fall, t_f, may be imposed to discourage fall application. This tax must be sufficient so that when it is added to r_f,

$$(3.9)\qquad (d_1 - e_1)/(1 - e_3) \le (r_f + t_f)/r_g.$$

This guarantees that a farmer endeavoring to maximize his or her expected utility of net farm income (profit) will not apply nitrogen fertilizer in the fall.

(c) Nitrogen Fertilizer Application When Growing-Season Application May be Possible

Uncertainty as to the condition of the field at the time of planting appears to play a significant role in a farmer's decision concerning nitrogen fertilizer application timing

---

10 The mechanics are left to the reader. The details are similar to those found in the previous footnote.

11 It has been suggested that this policy be promoted in order to minimize nitrogen fertilizer runoff into surface water and to reduce nitrate leaching into the ground water. Blackmer [1987], among others, discusses this in more detail.

(Feinerman et al. [1990] and Stan and Hinkle [1987]). A farmer practices a fall or spring application because he or she assigns a nonzero probability to the likelihood that nitrogen fertilizer application will not be possible after planting. It is assumed that the farmer assigns the probability P that he or she will be unable to apply nitrogen fertilizer after planting. This P is used as the basis for determining application timing and the amount of nitrogen fertilizer applied to maximize expected net farm income.

When growing-season application of nitrogen fertilizer may be possible (i.e., $0 < P < 1$), the first order conditions from (3.5) can be used to illustrate that a split nitrogen fertilizer application can be optimal whereby some nitrogen fertilizer is applied prior to planting and some after planting. In what follows, the necessary condition for a split application to be optimal will be developed. Fall and growing-season split application is used as the example. The result is easy to generalize.

To develop the necessary condition for a split application of nitrogen fertilizer to be optimal, first move r_f in the first relationship in (3.5) to the right-hand-side and also move the term involving r_g in the third relationship in (3.5) to the right-hand-side. Then divide the first relationship by the third to obtain

(3.10) $$((d_1 - e_1)/(1 - e_3))(1 - P + (P\,(\partial Y(N_a, W|\,V, N_g{=}0)/\partial N_a)/(\partial Y(N_a, W|\,V)/\partial N_a))) \le r_f/r_g.$$

This relationship suggests the optimal nitrogen fertilizer application rates for the fall and growing-seasons. If a fall/growing-season split application is optimal, then the ratio of the marginal physical product for fall applied nitrogen fertilizer and growing-season nitrogen fertilizer applied, $(\partial Y(N_a, W|\,V, N_g{=}0)/\partial N_a)/(\partial Y(N_a, W|\,V)/\partial N_a))$, will be greater than or equal to 1. Note that $\partial Y(N_a, W|\,V, N_g{=}0)/\partial N_a$ is equal to $(d_1 - e_1)\partial Y(N_a, W|\,V, N_g{=}0)/\partial N_f$, the marginal physical product of nitrogen fertilizer applied in the fall discounted by nitrogen fertilizer losses.

Next, for given values of P, d_1, d_2, e_1, e_2, and e_3, the necessary condition for a fall/growing-season split fertilizer application to be optimal is for the adjusted fall nitrogen fertilizer cost to be greater than the adjusted growing-season nitrogen fertilizer cost. That is, a fall/growing season split application will be optimal when

(3.11) $$r_f/(d_1 - e_1) \ge r_g/(1 - e_3).$$

This is demonstrated in what follows. In relationship (3.10), let $K_1 = ((d_1 - e_1)/(1 - e_3))$ which is less than 1[12] and let $K_2 = (r_f/r_g)$ which also less than or equal to one (National Agricultural Statistics Service [1991]). Also, let $K_3 = (1 - P + (P\,(\partial Y(N_a, W|\,V, N_g{=}0)/\partial N_a)/(\partial Y(N_a, W|\,V)/\partial N_a)))$. Then relationship (3.10) can be expressed as $K_1 K_3 \le K_2$. If a split application is optimal, K_3 will be greater than one for P not equal to zero because $(\partial Y(N_a, W|\,V, N_g{=}0)/\partial N_a)/(\partial Y(N_a, W|\,V)/\partial N_a)$ is always greater than or equal to one as noted above. For K_3 is greater than one, K_1 will have to be less than K_2 in order for

12 This is empirically verified below.

a split fertilizer application to occur. That is, for $K_3 > 1$, $(d_1 - e_1)/(1 - e_3) \leq r_f/r_g$. Rearranging terms yields relationship (3.11) which implies that the adjusted nitrogen cost (adjusted for nitrogen losses) for nitrogen fertilizer applied during the growing season must be less than the adjusted cost of nitrogen applied in the fall when the perceived probability that the farmer will not be able to apply nitrogen fertilizer during the growing season, P, is greater than 0 and less than 1 in order for a split application of nitrogen fertilizer to be optimal. Intuitively, if the adjusted cost of nitrogen fertilizer applied during the growing season is greater than the price for fall applied nitrogen fertilizer, the farmer would plan to apply all his or her nitrogen fertilizer in the fall to ensure that nitrogen would be available for plant uptake.

Furthermore, it would be increasingly likely that a farmer would apply nitrogen fertilizer only during the growing season as the adjusted price of nitrogen fertilizer applied during the growing season becomes smaller relative to the adjusted price of fall applied nitrogen fertilizer. In fact, using the first and the third relationships in (3.5), it can be shown that a farmer would **not** apply nitrogen fertilizer in the fall if

$$(3.12)\quad (\partial Y(N_a, W| V, N_g{=}0)/\partial N_a)\, P < (r_f/(p_c\,(d_1 - e_1)) - (r_g/p_c\,(1 - e_3)))\,(1 - P).$$

That is, when the perceived probability of not being able to apply nitrogen fertilizer during the growing season is P for $0 < P < 1$, nitrogen fertilizer will not be applied in the fall by a risk neutral, profit maximizing farmer when the expected marginal physical product of nitrogen fertilizer applied in the fall is less than the expected adjusted price of nitrogen fertilizer applied in the fall after subtracting the expected adjusted cost of growing-season applied nitrogen fertilizer.

A FARM-LEVEL DECISION MODEL WITH RISK AVERSION

The foregoing section analyzed the timing of the application of nitrogen fertilizer assuming a farmer endeavoring to maximize expected utility of net farm income is risk neutral. Now, the analysis will be altered by assuming that the farmer is risk averse. With P defined as the perceived probability that field conditions will not allow nitrogen fertilizer to be applied after planting, the expected utility function of a risk averse, profit maximizing farmer can be expressed as

$$(3.13)\quad Z = E\,[U(\pi)] = U(\pi_1)\,(1 - P) + U(\pi_2)\,P$$

where $\pi_1 = p_c\,Y(N_a, W| V) - r_f\,N_f - r_s\,N_s - r_g\,N_g - r_w\,W - OC$,

$\pi_2 = p_c\,Y(N_a, W| V, N_g{=}0) - r_f\,N_f - r_s\,N_s - r_w\,W - OC$, and

the other terms are as previously defined.

In this formulation of the problem as in the risk neutral case, it is assumed that the farmer is endeavoring to maximize expected utility of net farm income where net farm income is dependent on the timing of nitrogen fertilizer application. The formulation does not consider the impact on net farm income due to uncertainty in the price of nitrogen fertilizer associated with seasonal variations.

The first order conditions for the optimal nitrogen fertilizer application rates and irrigation, N_f, N_s, N_g, W - which are variables over which the farmer has control - are[13]

$$\partial Z/\partial N_f = U'(\pi_1)(\pi_c\,(d_1 - e_1)(\partial Y(N_a, W|V)/\partial N_a) - r_f)(1 - P)$$
$$+ U'(\pi_2)(\pi_c\,(d_1 - e_1)(\partial Y(N_a, W|V, N_g{=}0)/\partial N_a) - r_f]\,P$$
$$\leq 0$$

$$(3.14)\quad \partial Z/\partial N_s = U'(\pi_1)(\pi_c\,(d_2 - e_2)(\partial Y(N_a, W|V)/\partial N_a) - r_s)(1 - P)$$
$$+ U'(\pi_2)(\pi_c\,(d_2 - e_2)(\partial Y(N_a, W|V, N_g{=}0)/\partial N_a) - r_s)\,P$$
$$\leq 0$$

$$\partial Z/\partial N_g = \pi_c\,(1 - e_3)(\partial Y(N_a, W|V)/\partial N_a) - r_g \leq 0$$

$$\partial Z/\partial W = U'(\pi_1)(\pi_c\,\partial Y(N_a, W|V)/\partial W) - r_w)(1 - P)$$
$$+ U'(\pi_2)(\pi_c\,\partial Y(N_a, W|V)/\partial W) - r_w)\,P \leq 0.$$

Note that if the after-planting application of nitrogen fertilizer is not possible (i.e., $P = 1$), the first order conditions for the optimal nitrogen fertilizer application rates for a risk averse farmer are the same as the conditions for a risk neutral farmer. Similarly, if the after-planting application is always possible (i.e., $P = 0$), the first order conditions for the optimal nitrogen fertilizer application rates are same as the conditions for a risk neutral farmer. Also note that the third relationship in (3.14) indicates that the optimal amount of nitrogen fertilizer that should be applied during the growing season is not affected by the nature of the utility function specified for a farmer maximizing the expected utility of net farm income.

When growing-season application of nitrogen fertilizer may be possible (i.e., $0 < P < 1$), the optimal rates for the fall and growing-season application of nitrogen fertilizer can be derived. (As before, in order to simplify the exposition, just the fall/growing season split is considered. The generalization of the results to include spring application is straightforward.) The optimal application rates for split fall/growing-season applications are given by

$$(3.15)\quad ((d_1 - e_1)/(1 - e_3))((1 - P + P\,(U'(\pi_2)/U'(\pi_1))$$
$$((\partial Y(N_a, W|V|N_g{=}0)/\partial N_a)/(\partial Y(N_a, W|V)/\partial N_a)))/(1 - P$$
$$+ P\,(U'(\pi_2)/U'(\pi_1))) \leq r_f/r_g$$

In order to give the relationship an empirical measure, it is necessary to introduce a functional form for the utility function. A utility function that is frequently used and one

[13] Note that U' denotes the first derivative of the farmer's utility function with respect to the decision variable.

that is mathematically tractable is one with constant relative risk aversion - $U(\pi)=\pi^{(1-R)}/(1-R)$ where R is a measure of risk aversion and $0 \leq R$.[14] This utility function has been suggested as one providing an appropriate structure for investigating risk in supply response analyses (Newbery and Stiglitz [1981] and Pope and Just [1991]).

Given this functional specification for the farmer's utility function, the ratio $U'(\pi_2)/U'(\pi_1)$ is equal to $(\pi_1/\pi_2)^R$. Substituting this into relationship (3.15), the relationship can be rewritten as

$$(3.16)\quad ((d_1 - e_1)/(1 - e_3))\ (((1 - P + P\ (\pi_1/\pi_2)^R \\ (\partial Y(N_a, W|\ V, N_g{=}0)/\partial N_a)/(\partial Y(N_a, W|\ V)/\partial N_a))/ \\ (1 - P + P\ (\pi_1/\pi_2)^R)) \leq r_f/r_g.$$

Note that relationship (3.16) becomes relationship (3.10) when the farmer is risk neutral (i.e., R = 0). Using an argument similar to that for when a farmer is risk neutral, it can be shown that relationship (3.11) is also a necessary condition for an optimal split fall/growing-season nitrogen fertilizer application for a risk averse farmer when P is greater than 0 and less than 1.[15]

So far it has been shown that if the necessary condition (relationship (3.11)) holds, a split application of nitrogen fertilizer is the optimal strategy for both risk neutral and risk averse farmers when $0 < P < 1$. Next, the question of whether a risk averse farmer will apply more nitrogen fertilizer in the fall than a risk neutral farmer if both risk averse and risk neutral farmers have the same values for d, e, P and yield response to N_a will be addressed. If this is the case, will the term $(\partial Y(N_a, W|\ V, N_g{=}0))/(\partial N_a/\partial Y(N_a, W|\ V)/\partial N_a)$ be larger for a risk neutral farmer than for a risk averse farmer at their respective optimal level of N_a? In what follows, it will be shown that a risk averse farmer will apply more nitrogen fertilizer in the fall than will a risk neutral farmer.

To simplify the exposition, assume that each of the relationships in (3.11) hold with equality. From the third relationship, $\partial Y(N_a, W|\ V)/\partial N_a = r_g/(\pi_c\ (1 - e_3))$. Substitute this expression for $\partial Y(N_a, W|\ V)/\partial N_a$ in the first relationship. Rearranging terms, the first relationship can be expressed as

$$(3.17)\quad \partial Y(N_a, W|\ V, N_g{=}0)/\partial N_a = r_f/(\pi_c\ (d_1 - e_1)) \\ - (\pi_2/\pi_1)^R\ (r_g/(\pi_c\ (1 - e_3)) \\ - r_f/(\pi_c\ (d_1 - e_1)))\ (1 - P)/P.$$

---

14 The farmer is risk neutral when R = 0.

15 Let $K_1 = (d_1 - e_1)/(1 - e_3)$, $K_2 = r_f/r_g$, and $K_3 = (((1 - P + P\ (\pi_1/\pi_2)^R\ ((\partial Y(Na, W|\ V, Ng{=}0)/\partial Na)/(\partial Y(Na, W|\ V)/\partial Na)))/(1 - P + P\ (\pi_1/\pi_2)^R))$. Then, $K_1 K_3 = K_2$. If a split nitrogen fertilizer application is optimal, then the term $(\partial Y(N_a, W|\ V, N_g{=}0)/(\partial N_a)/\partial Y(N_a, W|\ V)/\partial N_a))$ will be greater than 1 which implies that K_3 is greater than 1. If K_3 is greater than 1, then K_1 must be less than K_2.

Observe that equation (3.17) employs the utility function with constant relative risk aversion. Since $R > 0$ for a risk averse farmer and $R = 0$ for a risk neutral farmer, the difference in the marginal physical product of fall applied nitrogen fertilizer, for a given level of N_a, between a risk averse farmer and a risk neutral farmer can be computed. This difference is given as

$$(3.18)\quad (\partial Y(N_a, W| V, N_g{=}0)/\partial N_a)_n - (\partial Y(N_a, W| V, N_g{=}0)/\partial N_a)_a$$
$$= - (1 - (\pi_2/\pi_1)^R)\,((r_g/[\pi_c (1 - e_3)) - r_f/(\pi_c (d_1 - e_1)))(1 - P)/P$$

where subscripts n and a denote a risk neutral and risk averse farmer, respectively. From equation (3.18), it can be seen that if the adjusted fall nitrogen fertilizer cost, $r_f/(d_1 - e_1)$, is greater than the adjusted growing-season nitrogen fertilizer cost, $r_g/(1 - e_3)$, for a given π_c, then $(\partial Y(N_a, W| V, N_g{=}0)/\partial N_a)_n - (\partial Y(N_a, W| V, N_g{=}0)/\partial N_a)_a$ is greater than 0. This is because $(\pi_2/\pi_1)^R < 1$. Therefore, a risk averse farmer will tend to allocate relatively more nitrogen fertilizer for fall application than will a risk neutral farmer, all other things equal.

This result has an intuitive explanation by using the fact that a risk neutral farmer maximizes expected net farm income while a risk averse farmer simultaneously maximizes expected net farm income and minimizes the variance of net farm income (Newbery and Stiglitz [1981]). When the adjusted fall nitrogen fertilizer cost increases relative to the adjusted growing-season nitrogen fertilizer cost, a risk neutral farmer in attempting to maximize the expected utility of net farm income will reduce his or her fall nitrogen fertilizer application and increase the growing-season application. As the fall nitrogen fertilizer application rate is reduced and more nitrogen fertilizer is applied during the growing season, the difference between net farm incomes π_1 and π_2 increases. Consequently, the variance of net farm income, $P (1 - P)(\pi_1 - \pi_2)^2$ increases.[16] Since a risk averse farmer would also attempt to minimize this variance, he or she will be more reticent than the risk neutral farmer to reduce the application of nitrogen fertilizer in the fall and increase growing-season application. Therefore, a risk averse farmer is likely to apply more nitrogen fertilizer in the fall than a risk neutral farmer when the adjusted fall nitrogen fertilizer price increases relative to the growing-season price. Furthermore, if both risk neutral and risk averse farmers are able to apply nitrogen fertilizer during the growing season, each will equate $\pi_c (1 - e_3)(\partial Y(N_a, W| V)/\partial N_a)$ with r_g (from the third relationship in (3.14)). Assuming N_a is the same between farmers, a risk averse farmer would apply less nitrogen fertilizer during the growing season than would a risk neutral farmer.

Next, from equation (3.18), if the adjusted fall nitrogen fertilizer cost is less than the adjusted growing-season nitrogen fertilizer cost, $(\partial Y(N_a, W| V, N_g{=}0)/\partial N_a)_n$ is less than

---

16 Given the net farm income random variable π_1 with a probability of occurring of P and the net farm income random variable π_2 with a probability of occurring of (1-P), expected net farm income $E[\pi] = \pi_1 P + \pi_2 (1 - P)$. The variance of expected net farm income, $V(\pi) = E[\pi^2] - (E[\pi])^2 = P (1 - P)(\pi_1 - \pi_2)^2$. Newbery and Stiglitz [1981] develop this and other relationships.

$(\partial Y(N_a, W| V, N_g=0)/\partial N_a)_a$. Thus, a risk averse farmer, in contrast to a risk neutral farmer, thus, would tend allocate relatively less nitrogen fertilizer for a given level of N_a for fall application.

Additionally, as P approaches 1, the term (1 - P)/P in equation (3.18) approaches 0. Consequently, the difference in the fall nitrogen fertilizer application by a risk neutral farmer and by a risk averse farmer will become small. Alternatively, as P increases, π_2/π_1 approaches 1 because more nitrogen fertilizer will be applied in the fall and less during the growing season. This implies that the term $(\pi_2/\pi_1)^R$ in equation (3.18) will approach 1. As a result, the difference in nitrogen fertilizer application rates between seasons by a risk averse and by a risk neutral farmer becomes insignificant regardless of the value of R.

The foregoing two sections have developed the necessary conditions for the optimal timing of nitrogen fertilizer application for a risk neutral and a risk averse farmer. In what follows, these necessary conditions will be used to explore the timing decisions of cotton farmers in the United States.

Estimating Nitrogen Fertilizer Losses

(a) Background

In order to empirically implement the farm-level decision models developed, estimates of nitrogen losses associated with the timing of nitrogen fertilizer application is needed. Before developing these estimates, however, the data used in the estimation will be discussed.

As part of the President's Water Quality Initiative, the U.S. Department of Agriculture's Economic Research Service (ERS) and National Agricultural Statistics Service (NASS) conducted a survey of cotton producers in 14 Southern and Western States in 1989 (Crutchfield et al. [1990]). The survey accounted for cotton production on 10.5 million acres. This is about 99 percent of the total planted cotton acreage in the United States. Information on eleven different aspects of cotton production was obtained. There were questions on yield, fertilizer use, herbicides and insecticides applied, irrigation practices employed, water availability, government program participation, value of the cropland on which cotton was produced, pest management practices employed, operator characteristics and soil characteristics. The fertilizer use section collected data on fertilizer application rates in the fall and spring (both pre-planting periods), coincident with planting and during the growing season (i.e., post-planting). The soil characteristic section collected information on the soil texture for each field surveyed classified according to the Soils-5 criteria (Soil Conservation Service [1983]). The survey yielded 1491 useable responses.

Cotton farmers in the United States practice single and split nitrogen fertilizer applications. Of the total number of cotton producers responding to the survey, 315 (21.1%) had a single nitrogen fertilizer application in the spring, 280 (18.8%) applied nitrogen fertilizer in the spring and during the growing season, and 213 (14.3%) of those surveyed applied no nitrogen fertilizer. Additionally, 67.4% of cotton farmers applied nitrogen fertilizer in the fall or in the spring but few (0.6%) applied it in both the fall and spring. Many cotton producers surveyed (32.4%) practice split applications whereby the application of nitrogen fertilizer was split before and after planting. Finally, most farmers applied some fertilizer during the growing season (78.1%). Note that these percentages sum to more that 100% since some farmers applied nitrogen fertilizer in more than one period.

The nitrogen fertilizer application rate varies significantly across application timing. For example, farmers applying nitrogen fertilizer during the fall as well as the planting and growing seasons applied an average of 253 pounds per acre (although the sample is small so any inferences are obviously suspect) while farmers applying nitrogen fertilizer during the planting and growing seasons applied an average of 120 pounds per acre.

(b) Cotton Yield Function Estimate

Estimates of nitrogen losses associated with the timing of nitrogen fertilizer application are needed. To this end, a production function approach will be used to estimate nitrogen losses for nitrogen fertilizer applied. The approach estimates a cotton yield function designed to show the relationship between the amount and timing of nitrogen fertilizer applied and cotton yield. Because the functional specification of the yield function can affect the estimates, several commonly used specifications were considered in order to test the robustness of the estimates (Cerrato and Blackmer [1987] and [Frank et al. [1990]). The purpose in using several different functional forms was not to compare the performance of one against the others. Rather, it was to assist in deciding whether the integrity of the conclusions with regard to nitrogen fertilizer application timing are such as to withstand scrutiny if the estimates are subject to a robustness test. Also, different functional specifications permit a comparison of the magnitudes of the estimated nitrogen fertilizer losses from the various functional forms to see whether there is any consistency. Three functional forms were tested. These were a quadratic specification, Mitscherlich-Baule functional form, and a von Liebig-type specification. While each functional form is considerably different from the others (they were selected because of this), each is relatively parsimonious and imposes certain technical characteristics on the yield response curve. (Frank et al. [1990] discusses these considerations in greater detail).

Nonlinear least squares was used to estimate the parameters for each cotton yield function specification. An examination of the matrix of correlation coefficients indicated no significant collinearity was present among the explanatory variables. Additionally, the variance-decomposition proportions (Belsley, Kuh, and Welsch [1980] were uniformly relatively small. The proportions never exceed 0.30 and typically average around 0.01 to 0.05. Using the adjusted coefficient of determination (i.e., R^2) and the Davidson-MacKinnon J-test as evaluation criteria, the quadratic specification, among those considered, best characterizes the relationship between factor inputs and cotton output (yield) with the von Liebig function being slightly behind in explanatory power.

The estimate of the quadratic yield function is given in Table 3.1. Note that since cotton yield is determined not only by the amount of nitrogen fertilizer available for plant uptake during the growing season, N_a, but also by site specific characteristics, variables to reflect these site specific considerations are included in the yield function specification to reflect yield variation due to these factors. Site specific variables include IR which is a variable indicating whether irrigation occurs (i.e., IR = 1) or does not occur (i.e., IR = 0),[17] WC which measures the water holding capacity of the soil, SL which calibrates the slope of the field, PC which is a variable indicating whether the previous crop was cotton (i.e., PC = 1) or some other crop (PC = 0), RF which is an index of the rainfall as defined by Wischmeier and Smith [1978], SP which is a measure of the soil permeability, and OM which is a measure of the organic matter content of the soil. The other variables found in the table are defined as they were previously.

Table 3.1. Estimated Quadratic Cotton Yield Function[1]

$$Y = \underset{(63.21)}{315.20} + \underset{(39.43)}{118.58}\ IR + \underset{(319.47)}{186.83}\ WC - \underset{(691.11)}{1207.78}\ SL - \underset{(22.10)}{13.66}\ PC$$

$$+ \underset{(0.1203)}{0.1197}\ RF - \underset{(4.54)}{3.95}\ SP + \underset{(18.90)}{208.49}\ W - \underset{(2.52)}{22.12}\ W^2 - \underset{(14.03)}{16.47}\ OM$$

$$+ \underset{(0.3732)}{0.8779}\ W\,[N_f\,(\underset{(0.1920)}{0.5792} - \underset{(0.2142)}{0.2821}\ IR) + (N_s + N_p)\,(\underset{(0.1501)}{0.5920} - \underset{(0.1614)}{0.4041}\ IR)$$

$$+ N_g\,(1 - \underset{(0.1932)}{0.5763}\ IR)]$$

$$+ \underset{(0.8531)}{5.4724}\,[N_f\,(\underset{(0.1904)}{0.5790} - \underset{(0.2112)}{0.2828}\ IR) + (N_s + N_p)\,(\underset{(0.1515)}{0.5924} - \underset{(0.1604)}{0.4040}\ IR)$$

$$+ N_g\,(1 - \underset{(0.1930)}{0.5761}\ IR)]$$

$$- \underset{(0.8544)}{0.02373}\,[N_f\,(\underset{(0.1922)}{0.5792} - \underset{(0.2100)}{0.2824}\ IR) + (N_s + N_p)\,(\underset{(0.1514)}{0.5921} - \underset{(0.1661)}{0.4040}\ IR)$$

$$+ N_g\,(1 - \underset{(0.1931)}{0.5761}\ IR)]^2$$

Adjusted $R^2 = 0.5232$ MSE = 79960.0

[1] The values in parentheses are the standard errors of the estimates.

[17] This implies that with irrigation, the production function shifts from what it would be with no irrigation.

The quadratic yield function indicates the presence of diminishing marginal returns with respect to the amount of nitrogen fertilizer applied and with respect to irrigation. Moreover, the results suggest that irrigation and nitrogen fertilizer use are complementary inputs. All of the signs on the terms involving nitrogen fertilizer application rates and associated with application timing and those associated with irrigation are consistent with *a priori* expectations. For example, an increase in the nitrogen fertilizer application rate in any period will result in an expansion in the cotton yield while an increase in irrigation likewise will yield an increase cotton output. Moreover, given that cross-section data are being used, the quadratic specification fits the data reasonably well.

Before examining the issue of application timing and nitrogen fertilizer losses, consider the impacts of site specific factors on cotton yield. To this end, consider first the effect of the presence or absence of irrigation. As expected, the quadratic functional specification shows that the irrigation variable is statistically significant at the 5% level indicating that irrigated cropland in general has a higher cotton yield than non-irrigated cropland. This is because irrigation promotes nutrient movement to the root by diffusion and mass flow (Rhoads [1984]).

The coefficient on water holding capacity is positive but not significantly different from zero at the 5% level. A positive sign was anticipated on this variable suggesting that soil with a higher water holding capacity would produce a higher yield. This result is expected because the agronomy literature illustrates that a higher water holding capacity is linked to higher productivity (Metcalfe and Elkins [1980]). Also, a higher water holding capacity can increase nutrient concentration in the soil and enhance the rate of nutrient movement to the root by diffusion and mass flow (Rhoads [1984]).

The coefficient on the slope of the cropland variable is negative but not statistically significantly different from zero at the 5% level. A statistically significant negative sign was expected because a greater slope promotes nitrogen loss by surface runoff leaving less nitrogen fertilizer for plant uptake and a coincident reduction in yield (Gilliam and Hoyt [1987]).

A negative sign on the coefficient estimate for the previous crop planted variable indicates that a reduction in cotton yield would be realized if the previous planted crop were cotton. This result is expected because the continuous planting of cotton promotes the propagation of insect pests such as the boll weevil which causes a loss of cotton yield (Stan and Hinkle [1987] and Metcalfe and Elkins [1980]). Unfortunately, the coefficient estimate on this variable was not statistically significant at the 5% level.

The sign on the coefficient of the rainfall index variable should be negative because the index is designed to quantify the impact of rainfall on soil erosion (Wischmeier and Smith [1978]). A reduction in yield is associated with increased soil loss (Taylor and Frohberg [1978]). The estimate, however, is not statistically significant at the 5% level or better.

The coefficient on soil permeability has a negative sign which is expected although it is not statistically significant at the 5% level. Soil with greater permeability has a larger potential for nitrate leaching thereby reducing the nitrogen available for plant uptake (Bock [1984]).

A relatively large amount of organic matter in the soil is often associated with elevated crop yields (Soil Conservation Service [1983]). Therefore, a positive sign is expected on the organic matter variable. The estimation results, however, yield a negative sign although the estimate is not statistically significant at the 5% level. A further examination of this result is warranted in subsequent research.

The impact of irrigation on cotton yield is statistically significant at the 5% level for the quadratic functional specification. The estimated coefficients on both the linear term and the quadratic term have the expected sign and are statistically significantly different than zero at the 5% level. The negative sign on the quadratic term indicates the presence of decreasing marginal returns with regard to the quantity of water applied.

(c) Nitrogen Fertilizer Losses and the Timing of Applications

To assess the nitrogen fertilizer losses associated with the timing of application, the empirical estimates from the cotton yield function are used. Nitrogen fertilizer losses, as defined earlier in relationship (3.2) and estimated in the cotton yield function, will be indicated by the proportion of nitrogen fertilizer applied before planting, which is not be available for plant uptake during the growing-season. The estimation results indicate that for dryland cotton production, fall and spring applications losses are approximately the same as the amount lost during the growing season. For example, fall application losses are about 0.42 (1-0.58) for each pound of nitrogen fertilizer applied while the spring application losses are about 0.41 (1-0.59) for each pound of nitrogen fertilizer applied. The difference in nitrogen fertilizer losses associated with these two application timings is not statistically significantly different than zero at the 5% level.

For irrigated cotton, the loss of nitrogen fertilizer applied during the spring and growing season is also statistically significant. Thus, for each pound of nitrogen fertilizer applied during the growing season, about 43 percent is available for plant uptake relative to growing-season nitrogen fertilizer applied in dryland cotton production. For each pound of nitrogen fertilizer applied in the spring, about 20 percent (0.592 - 0.404) is available during the growing season. Results for the fall application are not statistically significantly different than zero at the 5% level. These results show that irrigation is likely to cause additional nitrogen fertilizer loss for both spring and growing season applications.

(d) Nitrogen Fertilizer Losses and Irrigation

Irrigation results in a significant loss of nitrogen fertilizer in cotton production. The estimation results indicate that, in the presence of irrigation, about 0.58 pounds of nitrogen fertilizer is lost for each pound of nitrogen fertilizer applied during the growing season. When spring application is used, 0.40 of each pound of nitrogen fertilizer applied is lost when irrigation is practiced relative to no such losses for dryland cotton production.

It should be noted, however, that if nitrogen fertilizer is leached into the ground water, some indeterminate portion of the estimated loss may appear in the irrigation water and therefore be available for plant uptake. This is evidenced by the complementary relation between nitrogen fertilizer applied and irrigation as shown by the statistically significant at the 5% level coefficient estimate on the nitrogen application/irrigation cross product term. Also, some portion of the leached nitrogen fertilizer may contribute to the fertility of irrigated cropland (Spilker [1991]). This is evinced by the statistically significant at the 5% level coefficient estimate on the irrigation variable, IR. Unfortunately, given the way the information was collected on the Cotton Water Quality Survey, it is not possible to separate these effects from the estimated nitrogen fertilizer losses.

The combined timing and irrigation effects on nitrogen fertilizer losses show that spring nitrogen fertilizer application losses are no greater than fall application losses.

There are a variety of reasons why nitrogen fertilizer loss associated with fall application should be different than losses from a spring application. These include the fact that a relatively high carbon to nitrogen ratio during the fall favors immobilization of nitrates in the soil (Blackmer [1987]). Next, relatively high soil moisture content due to irrigation and spring rain leads to a relatively higher level of denitrification of newly applied nitrogen fertilizer. (Note that the denitrification process refers to the biological transformation of nitrogen in the nitrate or nitrite forms to gaseous forms that escape from the soil (Blackmer [1987]).) Finally, nitrogen fertilizer applied in the spring on the soil surface is more susceptible to runoff loss due rain, while nitrogen fertilizer applied in the fall is typically laid under the topsoil (Rhoads [1984]). These factors suggest that the application timing between fall and spring should have differential effects on cotton production. The fact that the empirical results suggest that it does not will be the subject of a future investigation. In what follows, we attempt to explain the current mixed single and split nitrogen fertilizer applications in U.S. cotton production.

ESTIMATION OF THE OPTIMAL APPLICATION TIMING OF NITROGEN FERTILIZER

Estimation of the optimal application timing using the cotton yield function estimate derived together with recent United States nitrogen fertilizer price data will now be presented. The results are based on the previously delineated farm-level decision models for a risk neutral and a risk averse farmer. Corresponding to the previous discussion concerning possible values of the perceived probability P, the discussion is divided into three sections.

A. Nitrogen Fertilizer Application When Growing-Season Application Is Not Possible

Relationship (3.6) is used to test the hypothesis that fall application is preferable to spring application assuming that the farmer is maximizing expected net farm income (utility) and that he or she is risk neutral (averse). For dryland cotton production, $d_1/d_2 = 0.58/0.59 = 0.98$. The price ratio is $r_f/r_s = 10.9/12.0 = 0.91$, where r_f is the United States average fall price in cents per pound of anhydrous ammonia in October 1990 and r_g is the

United States average April 1991 price (National Agricultural Statistics Service [1991]).[18] Since the value of d_1/d_2 (= 0.98) is greater than the nitrogen fertilizer price ratio (= 0.90), a fall application is preferable to a spring application. However, since these two ratios are not statistically significantly different from each other at the 5% level, an U.S. cotton farmer would likely be indifferent between a fall and spring application.[19]

For irrigated cotton, if irrigation has no effect on the loss of fall nitrogen (recall that e_1 was not statistically significantly different than from zero in the cotton yield function estimate), the value of $(d_1 - e_1)/(d_2 - e_2) = 0.58/0.19 = 3.05$. Since this value is much greater than the nitrogen fertilizer price ratio, a farmer would prefer a fall application to a spring application.

B. Nitrogen Fertilizer Application when Growing-Season Application is not Restricted

The hypothesis that growing-season application of nitrogen fertilizer is preferable to fall application for both dryland and irrigated cotton production cannot be rejected, if weather conditions do not inhibit the application of nitrogen fertilizer during the growing season. Using relationship (3.7), for fall fertilizer application for dryland cotton production, the value of $(d_1 - e_1)/(1 - e_3) = 0.58$ while for irrigated cotton production, the value is $(d_1 - e_1)/(1 - e_3) = 0.58/0.43 = 1.35$. These values suggest that for dryland cotton production, a growing-season application is preferable to a fall application since 0.58 is less than the fall/growing season nitrogen fertilizer price ratio of 0.91, even though the price of nitrogen fertilizer in the fall is lower than the price during the growing season. The nitrogen fertilizer loss from the fall application outweighs the gain due to the relatively lower nitrogen fertilizer price in the fall. For irrigated cotton production, a fall application is preferable to a growing-season application since $(d_1 - e_1)/(1 - e_3)$ (= 1.35) is greater than the nitrogen fertilizer price ratio. This finding simply reflects the fact that if some nitrogen fertilizer applied during growing season is lost due to irrigation, a fall nitrogen fertilizer application or a split fall and growing-season application is preferable.

Also considered are the hypotheses that growing-season nitrogen fertilizer application is preferable to a spring application for irrigated and dryland cotton production. These hypotheses are tested using relationship (3.8). The numerical results, the details of which are left to the reader, suggest that a growing season application is preferable to a spring application for both irrigated and dryland cotton production.

---

18 Only the nitrogen fertilizer cost is considered. Not included are operating costs. It is likely that operating costs differ between fall, spring and growing-season applications. Field operating costs are not included because reported estimates of fall, spring and growing-season operating costs are inexorably intertwined with nitrogen fertilizer costs since nitrogen fertilizer application frequently occurs coincidentally with field preparation (Mississippi Cooperative Extension Service [1987]). Any attempt to separate the costs (which run about \$5.00 per acre) would be purely arbitrary.

19 A further uncertainty not dealt with is how expectations concerning the spring nitrogen fertilizer price formulated prior to the fall application will impact a farmer's timing decision.

C. Nitrogen Fertilizer Application when Growing-Season Application may be Possible

In this section, the optimal timing of the application and amounts of nitrogen fertilizer to be applied are estimated when P is greater than 0 and less than 1. First, relationship (3.11) will be used to determine whether a split application is optimal. For dryland cotton production, the test is whether a fall and growing-season split application of nitrogen fertilizer is optimal. (Recall that in the previous section, a fall application was identified as optimal given the seasonal nitrogen price differential between the fall and spring.) Because $(d_1 - e_1)/(1 - e_3) = 0.58 < r_f/r_g = 0.91$, a fall/growing-season split application of nitrogen fertilizer is an optimal strategy for dryland cotton production. Furthermore, if there is no seasonal difference in the nitrogen fertilizer price, a cotton farmer would be indifferent between considering a fall/growing-season split and a spring/growing-season split application of nitrogen fertilizer as an optimal strategy. For irrigated cotton production, because $(d_2 - e_2)/(1 - e_3) = 0.44 < 1.0$,[20] a split application is the optimal strategy for both dryland and irrigated cotton production.

Next, the optimal nitrogen fertilizer application rates will be estimated. This will be accomplished by maximizing expected net farm income given by the objective function (4) of a risk neutral farmer. The estimated quadratic cotton yield function given in Table 3.1 is used in the computations. The optimal levels of N_f, N_s, and N_g are determined for various values of P.

To investigate the timing of nitrogen fertilizer application for a risk averse farmer, the constant relative risk aversion utility function previously introduced is employed. It will be assumed that $R = 1.5$.[21] In estimating π_1 and π_2, production costs for Texas dryland cotton and California irrigated cotton are used to estimate other costs, OC (McElroy et al. [1989]). The optimal levels of N_f, N_s, and N_g are determined for various values of P. The results for the dryland cotton are given in Table 3.2. The estimates in Table 3.2 lend credence to the contention that if the adjusted fall nitrogen cost ($r_f/d_1 = 10.9/0.57 = 19.1$) is greater than the adjusted growing-season nitrogen fertilizer cost, r_g, a risk averse farmer, in contrast to a risk neutral farmer, tends to allocate more nitrogen fertilizer for fall application. The results are consistent with the finding of Feinerman et al. [1990].

---

20 Spring and growing-seasons applications are used as an example because the e_2 of the spring application is significant, while the e_1 of the fall application is not significant.

21 There is nothing unique about this value. It is simply used for computational purposes. Alternative values can be considered.

Table 3.2. Nitrogen Fertilizer Application Rates and Timings in Dryland Cotton Production Under Constant Relative Risk Aversion $U = \pi^{(1-R)}/(1-R)$

Probability of failing to apply nitrogen fertilizer during growing-season		Risk-Neutral R = 0	Risk Averse R = 1.5
	Timing		
0	Fall	0	0
	Growing	112	112
0.10	Fall	152	160
	Growing	24	20
0.20	Fall	173	174
	Growing	12	11
0.30	Fall	180	181
	Growing	8	7
0.50	Fall	185	186
	Growing	5	5
0.75	Fall	188	189
	Growing	3	3
1.00	Fall	190	190
	Growing	0	0

In sum the empirical results confirm the theoretical contentions that in the case of dryland cotton production, when growing-season application of nitrogen fertilizer is not restricted, growing-season application is optimal. When growing-season application is not possible, then fall application is optimal. When growing-season application may be possible, a fall/growing-season split application is optimal. Analogous results hold for the case of irrigated cotton production. Next, the results validate the hypothesis that more nitrogen is applied for irrigated cotton production than for dryland cotton. This is done in order to compensate for the nitrogen losses due to irrigation.

The results also show that a farmer would plan to apply some nitrogen fertilizer after planting as long as growing-season application is possible. In practice, there is a minimum nitrogen fertilizer application rate needed for the activity to be economically justifiable. For example, for dryland cotton, if this minimum amount is 50 pounds per acre, a farmer would apply nitrogen fertilizer only in the fall (and probably would increase amount of nitrogen fertilizer applied to compensate for the expected losses) if P is greater than 0.1. Similarly, a farmer would apply nitrogen fertilizer during the growing-season if P is less than 0.05. These findings explain why both single and split nitrogen fertilizer applications are common practices among cotton producers in the United States.

Cotton farmers who irrigate are likely to apply some nitrogen fertilizer during the growing season. Irrigated cotton is typically grown in areas where rainfall is limited so that the likelihood of having wet field conditions which limit after-planting nitrogen fertilizer application is extremely small. Consequently, a farmer can maximize his or her expected net farm income by applying nitrogen fertilizer during the growing season. The Cotton Water Quality Survey data show that about 70 percent of the farmers surveyed who irrigated applied nitrogen fertilizer after planting, as compared with only 50 percent of dryland cotton producers who applied nitrogen fertilizer after planting.

Conclusions

Based on farm-level production decision models for a cotton producer in the United States, if a farmer's perceived probability of not being able to apply nitrogen during the growing season is between 0 and 1 exclusively, then a split application of nitrogen fertilizer is the optimal strategy for both a risk neutral and a risk averse farmer. Additionally, a risk averse farmer will apply more nitrogen fertilizer prior to planting than a risk neutral farmer. Consequently, any policy designed to promote a single application of nitrogen fertilizer during the growing season to minimize nitrogen fertilizer runoff into surface water and to reduce nitrate leaching into ground water would cause a farmer to move away from his or her optimal nitrogen fertilizer application strategy. This being the case, the farmer would have to have a sufficient incentive to change. This incentive could take a variety of forms including compensation.

References

Anderson, J., J. Dillon, and B. Hardaker, *Agricultural Decision Analysis*, The Iowa State University Press, Ames, IA, 1977.

Arrow, K., *Essays in the Theory of Risk-Bearing*, Markham Publishing Company, Chicago, IL, 1971.

Belsley, D., E. Kuh, and R. Welsch, *Regression Diagnostics*, John Wiley and Sons, Inc., New York, NY, 1980.

Blackmer, A., "Losses and Transport of Nitrogen from Soil," Chapter 5 in *Rural Groundwater Contamination*, edited by F. D'itri and L. Wolfson, Lewis Publishers, Inc., Chelsea, MI, 1987.

Bock B., "Efficient Use of Nitrogen in Cropping Systems," Chapter 18 in *Nitrogen in Crop Production*, American Society of Agronomy, Madison, WI, 1984.

Borch, K., *The Economics of Uncertainty*, Princeton University Press, Princeton, NJ, 1968.

Cantor, P., "Health Effects of Agrichemicals in Groundwater: What Do We Know ?" *Agricultural Chemicals and Groundwater Protection: Emerging Management and Policy*, Proceedings of a Conference held in St. Paul, Minnesota, October 22-23, 1988, pp. 21-32.

Cerrato, M. and A. Blackmer, "Comparison of Models for Describing Corn Yield Response to Nitrogen Fertilizer," *Agronomy Journal*, Vol. 82 (1990), pp. 138-143.

Crutchfield, S., M. Ribaudo, P. Setia, D. Letson, and L. Hansen, *Cotton Production and Water Quality: An Initial Assessment*, Staff Report AGES 9105, Resources and Technology Division, Economic Research Service, U. S. Department of Agriculture, Washington, DC, January 1991.

Davidson, R., and J. MacKinnon, "Several Tests for Model Specification in the Presence of Alternative Hypotheses," *Econometrica*, Vol. 49 (1981), pp. 781-793.

Deaton, A., and J. Muellbauer, *Economics and Consumer Behavior*, Cambridge University Press, Cambridge, 1980.

Environmental Protection Agency, *National Survey of Pesticides in Drinking Water Wells*, Phase I Report. EPA 570/9-90-015, Environmental Protection Agency, Washington, DC, November 1990.

Feinerman, E., E. Choi, and S. Johnson, "Uncertainty and Split Nitrogen Application in Corn Production," *American Journal of Agricultural Economics*, Vol. 72 (1990), pp. 975-984.

Frank, M., B. Beattie, and M. Embleton, "A Comparison of Alternative Crop Response Models," *American Journal of Agricultural Economics*, Vol. 72 (1990), pp. 598-603.

Freshwater Foundation, *Nitrates and Groundwater: A Public Health Concern*, The Freshwater Foundation's Health and Environment Network, Navarre, MN, 1988.

Fertilizer Institute, *The Fertilizer Handbook*, Second Edition, The Fertilizer Institute, Washington, DC, 1976.

Gilliam, J. and Hoyt G., "Effect of Conservation Tillage on the Fate and Transport of Nitrogen," Chapter 13 in *Effects of Conservation Tillage on Groundwater Quality*, Lewis Publishers, Inc., Chelsea, MI, 1987.

Kanwar, R., J. Baker, and D. Baker, "Tillage and Split N-Fertilizer Effects on Subsurface Drainage Water Quality and Crop Yields," *Transactions of the American Society of Agricultural Engineers*, Vol. 31 (1988), pp. 453-461.

McElroy, R., R. Dismukes, and M. Ali, *State-Level Costs of Production, 1987*, Agriculture and Rural Economy Division, Economic Research Service, U.S. Department of Agriculture, Washington, DC, March 1989.

Metcalfe, D. and D. Elkins, *Crop Production: Principles and Practices*, Fourth Edition, Macmillan Publishing Co., New York, NY, 1980.

Mississippi Cooperative Extension Service, *1987 Cotton Costs and Returns*, Agricultural Economics Report 20, Mississippi Agricultural and Forestry Experiment Station, Mississippi State University, Mississippi State, MS, December 1986.

National Agricultural Statistics Service, *Agricultural Prices*. National Agricultural Statistics Service, U.S. Department of Agriculture, Washington, 1991, 1999.

Newbery, D., and J. Stiglitz, *The Theory of Commodity Price Stabilization*, Clarendon Press, Oxford, 1981.

Nielsen, E. and L. Lee, *The Magnitude and Cost of Ground Water Contamination from Agricultural Chemicals: A National Perspective*, AER-576, Economic Research Service, U.S. Department of Agriculture, Washington, DC, October 1987.

Pope, R. and R. Just, "On Testing the Structure of Risk Preferences in Agricultural Supply Analysis," *American Journal of Agricultural Economics*, Vol. 73 (1991), pp. 743-748.

Rhoads, T., "Nitrogen or Water Stress: Their Interrelationships," Chapter 20 in *Nitrogen in Crop Production*, American Society of Agronomy, Madison, WI, 1984.

Soil Conservation Service, *Application of Soil Information: Part 603*, 430-VI-NSH, Soil Conservation Service, U.S. Department of Agriculture, Washington, DC, 1983.

Spilker, M., "Estimating Applied Nitrogen Equivalents with a Generalized Linear Response and Plateau Function," Paper presented at 1991 American Agricultural Economics Association Annual Meetings, Manhattan, KS, August 4-7, 1991.

Stan, G., and D. Hinkle, *Maintaining Cotton Yields Through Fertilizer and Crop Rotations*, Bulletin 340, Agricultural Experiment Station, University of New Mexico, Albuquerque, NM, 1987.

Taylor, C. and K. Frohberg, "The Welfare Effects of Erosion Controls, Banning Pesticides, and Limiting Fertilizer Application in the Corn Belt: Reply," *American Journal of Agricultural Economics*, Vol 60 (1978), pp. 560-561.

Taylor, H., "A Statistical Analysis of Fertilizer Application Rate Differences Between 1989 and 1990," *Agricultural Resources: Input Situation and Outlook Report* AR-21, Economic Research Service, U.S. Department of Agriculture, Washington, DC, February 1991.

Viets, F. and R. Hageman, *Factors Affecting the Accumulation of Nitrates in Soil, Water, and Plants*, Agricultural Handbook No. 413, Agricultural Research Service, U.S. Department of Agriculture, Washington, DC, November 1971.

White, W., *Sources of Nitrogen and Phosphorus*, Resource Washington, Inc., Washington, DC, June 1989.

Wischemeier, W. and D. Smith, *Predicting Rainfall Erosion Losses*, Agricultural Handbook Number 537, U.S. Department of Agriculture, Washington, DC, 1978.

Chapter 4

THE EFFECTS OF THE TIMING OF NITROGEN FERTILIZER APPLICATION AND IRRIGATION ON YIELD AND NITROGEN LOSS IN COTTON PRODUCTION

INTRODUCTION

To minimize the presence of an excess amount of nitrogen in the soil which in turn is available for leaching into the groundwater, a desirable objective is to use efficiently the nitrogen fertilizer applied in growing the crop. Efficiently using the nitrogen applied in the form of nitrogen fertilizer while at the same time minimizing the potential for groundwater contamination can be achieved by applying nitrogen fertilizer at the time when the plant needs nitrogen the most and when the potential for nitrogen loss to the environment is at a minimum. Experimental results have shown that switching from the pre-planting application of nitrogen fertilizer to a coincident or post-planting application can improve nitrogen use efficacy and reduce nitrogen loss (Bock [1984] and Kanwar et al. [1988]). Because of the experimental results, a restriction on the pre-planting (fall) application of nitrogen fertilizer has been considered a viable policy option to reduce nitrate leaching in areas where the groundwater is vulnerable to nitrate contamination (Central Platte Natural Resources District [1989]).

There are other factors besides timing that can affect the efficacy of nitrogen use by a plant, and that, therefore, can affect the efficacy with which nitrogen fertilizer is used thereby affecting the optimal application rate of nitrogen fertilizer. These include such site specific variables as soil texture, the prevailing nitrate level in the soil, chemical properties of the soil, and weather conditions (Viets and Hageman [1971] and Bock [1984]). A general policy of restricting the fall application of nitrogen fertilizer to protect groundwater may not be effective if site specific factors are not taken into consideration.

To properly assess the anticipated effects of nitrogen fertilizer use and the timing of application under various site specific conditions requires the use of actual production data reflecting the myriad of site specific considerations (Taylor et al. [1978]).

Given these foregoing considerations, the objective of what follows is, first, to investigate the effect of timing as well as irrigation on the efficacy of nitrogen fertilizer use and, second, to assess the impact that irrigation has on the presence of excess nitrogen in the soil at the end of the growing season. To capture the variation brought about by site specific factors, data collected through the Cotton Water Quality Survey conducted by the U.S. Department of Agriculture in 1989 will be used. This will allow for an estimation of the loss of nitrogen associated with nitrogen fertilizer applied in the fall and spring prior to planting and during the growing period across various growing (site specific) conditions. The survey data reflect the relative efficacy with which nitrogen is used when nitrogen fertilizer is applied at different times throughout the year (e.g., pre-planting and during the growing season).

The discussion is organized as follows: the next section details the variation in the timing of the application of nitrogen fertilizer for cotton production. The following section empirically examines the effect of timing on nitrogen fertilizer use. The next section discusses the empirical results and draws relevant inferences concerning the impact of the timing of the application of nitrogen fertilizer and the presence of excess nitrogen while the penultimate section investigates the effects of irrigation on the presence of excess nitrogen. A summary of the findings concludes the discussion.

FERTILIZER USE IN COTTON PRODUCTION

As part of the President's Water Quality Initiative, the U.S. Department of Agriculture's Economic Research Service (ERS) and National Agricultural Statistics Service (NASS) conducted a survey of cotton producers in 14 Southern and Western States in 1989 (Crutchfield et al. [1990]). The survey accounted for cotton production on 10.5 million acres or about 99 percent of the total U.S. planted cotton acreage. Information on eleven different aspects of cotton production was obtained. There were questions on yield, fertilizer use, herbicides and insecticides applied, irrigation practices employed, water availability, government program participation, value of the cropland on which cotton was produced, pest management practices employed, operator characteristics and soil characteristics. The fertilizer use section collected data on fertilizer application rates in the fall and spring (both pre-planting periods), coincident with planting and during the growing season (i.e., post-planting). The soil characteristics section collected information on the soil texture for each field surveyed classified according to the Soils-5 criteria (Soil Conservation Service [1983]). The survey yielded 1491 useable responses.

(a) Excess Nitrate in Cotton Production

Based on the survey results, about 72 million pounds of excess nitrogen fertilizer were applied in cotton production in the United States in 1989 (Table 4.1). Recall that excess nitrogen is defined as the difference between the amount of nitrogen applied via nitrogen fertilizer and the amount of nitrogen contained in the cotton and plant residual

Table 4.1. Estimated Excess Nitrogen Fertilizer in Cotton Producing States[1]

STATE	EXCESS NITROGEN FERTILIZER	PER-ACRE EXCESS NITROGEN FERTILIZER
	Million Pounds	Pounds/Acre
ALABAMA	1.1	57
ARIZONA	3.0	137
ARKANSAS	3.4	58
CALIFORNIA	15.0	67
GEORGIA	0.4	36
LOUISIANA	3.4	57
MISSISSIPPI	12.0	73
MISSOURI	0.5	61
NEW MEXICO	0.06	26
NORTH CAROLINA	0.02	12
OKLAHOMA	0.3	17
SOUTH CAROLINA	0.3	68
TENNESSEE	1.9	57
TEXAS	31.0	19

[1] The excess nitrogen for each state is estimated by the following equation:

$$N_e = (N_1 + N_2 + N_3 + N_4) - \text{Yield}/1500 * 75$$

where N_i,i=1, 2, 3, 4 is the amount of nitrogen applied in fall, spring, planting and growing seasons, Yield is amount of cotton harvested, 75 is the number of pounds of active ingredients of nitrogen in 1500 pounds of cotton and in 2000 pounds of stalks, leaves and burs removed from the field (The Fertilizer Institute [1976]). The estimate from each producer in the sample is weighted by his or her contribution to surveyed production. The weighted estimates are then summed to obtain the state level estimates. It is assumed that stalks are produced in a fixed proportion to the cotton yield across all states and that all plant residues are removed from the field after harvest.

removed from the field at the end of the growing season. Among major cotton producing states, Texas has the largest amount of excess nitrogen, followed by California and Mississippi. Arizona, however, has the highest per ace rate of excess nitrogen, followed by Mississippi. North Carolina has the smallest per acre rate. Although Texas has the largest total quantity of excess nitrogen, it has a relatively small per acre rate.

(b) Application Timings and Rates

Table 4.2 presents the distribution of the survey responses according to the application timing of nitrogen fertilizer. Of the total number of cotton producers responding to the survey, 315 (21.1%) have a single nitrogen fertilizer application in the spring, 280 (18.8%) apply nitrogen fertilizer in the spring and during the growing period, and 213 (14.3%) of those surveyed apply no nitrogen fertilizer. Additionally, as Table 4.2 illustrates, 67.4% of cotton farmers apply fertilizer in the fall or in the spring but few (0.6%) apply it in both the fall and spring. Many cotton producers surveyed (32.4%) practice split applications whereby the application of nitrogen fertilizer is split before and after planting. Finally, most farmers apply some fertilizer during the growing period (78.1%).

Table 4.2. Numbers of Observations and Nitrogen Fertilizer Application Rates by Application Timing

Application Timing					
Fall	Spring	Planting	Growing	Number of Observations	Application Rate (lbs.)
				213 (14)[1]	0
				214 (14)	105
		x		27 (2)	58
		x	x	32 (2)	120
	x			317 (21)	62
	x		x	280 (19)	112
	x	x		33 (2)	83
	x	x	x	14 (1)	144
x				195 (13)	63
x			x	138 (9)	122
x		x		15 (1)	101
x		x	x	3 (0)	253
x	x			10 (1)	102
361 (24)	654 (43)	124 (8)	681 (46)		

[1] The value in parentheses is the percent of the total sample that represented.

The nitrogen fertilizer application rate varies significantly across application timing. For example, farmers applying nitrogen fertilizer during the fall as well as the planting and growing seasons apply an average of 253 pounds per acre (although the sample is small so any inferences are obviously suspect) while farmers applying nitrogen fertilizer during the planting and growing periods apply an average of 120 pounds per acre.

ALTERNATIVE MODELS OF THE PRODUCTION OF COTTON

Recall that the stated objectives were to investigate the effect of timing and irrigation on the effectiveness of nitrogen fertilizer applied in the production of cotton in the United States and to examine the impact of irrigation on the presence of excess nitrogen in the soil at the end of the growing season. To this end, a production function approach to estimate nitrogen losses associated with the timing of nitrogen fertilizer applied in cotton production will be used. Because the functional specification of the yield function can affect the estimates, three commonly used specifications in order to test the robustness of the estimates will be employed (Cerrato and Blackmer [1987] and Frank et al. [1990]). The purpose in using several different functional forms is not to compare the performance of one against the others. Rather, it is to assist in deciding whether the integrity of the conclusions with regard to nitrogen fertilizer application timing and irrigation are such as to withstand scrutiny if the estimates are subject to a robustness test. Also, the magnitudes of the estimated nitrogen fertilizer losses from various functional forms will be compared to see whether there is any consistency. The three functional forms tested are a quadratic specification, Mitscherlich-Baule functional form, and a von Liebig-type specification. While each functional form is considerably different from the others, each is relatively parsimonious and imposes certain technical characteristics on the yield response curve. Each of the functional forms is outlined below.

Define the nitrogen fertilizer available during the growing season, N_a, as

$$(4.1) \quad N_a = N_f (d_1 - e_1\, IR) + N_s (d_2 - e_2\, IR) + N_g (1 - e_3\, IR)$$

where N_f, N_s, and N_g are the amounts of nitrogen applied in the fall, spring, and during the growing period, respectively. The parameters d_1 and d_2 are the fraction of, respectively, the fall and spring nitrogen fertilizer available during the growing period. The parameters e_1, e_2, and e_3 are the fraction of the fall, spring and growing period nitrogen fertilizer lost through irrigation, if irrigation results in nitrogen leaching out of the root zone. The parameters e_1, e_2, and e_3 are zero for non-irrigated cotton. The variable IR is equal to 1 for irrigated cotton and 0 for non-irrigated cotton.

(a) Quadratic Function

The quadratic yield function is expressed as

$$(4.2) \quad Y = g + a_1 N_a + a_2 N_a^2 + a_3 W + a_4 W^2 + a_5 (W N_a) + e$$

where Y is the per acre cotton yield, N_a is the nitrogen fertilizer available during the growing season (as defined by relationship (4.1)), W is the irrigation rate, a_1, a_2, a_3, a_4, and a_5 are parameters to be estimated, and e is an error term that is identically and independently distributed with a zero mean and a finite and constant variance. The variable g is used to reflect the impact of the site specific characteristics that potentially serve to effect yield.

The quadratic function exhibits both increasing and decreasing marginal returns with regard to nitrogen fertilizer use and irrigation and complementarily or substitutability between the factor inputs N_a and W.

(b) Mitscherlich-Baule Function

The Mitscherlich-Baule yield function is expressed as:

$$(4.3) \qquad Y = g\,(1 - \exp(a_1\, N_a))\,(1 - (\exp(a_2\, W))\, IR) + e$$

where IR is 1 for irrigated cotton production and 0 for non-irrigated cotton production and the rest of the terms are as previously defined. The Mitscherlich-Baule function is appealing for its functional flexibility concerning input substitution and because it delineates a yield plateau (Cerrato and Blackmer [1987]).

(c) Von Liebig Function

The von Liebig yield function is expressed as:

$$(4.4) \qquad Y = g + \text{Min}\,(T,\, a_1 + a_2\, N_a\,,\, (a_3 + a_4\, W)\, IR + L\,(1 - IR)) + e$$

where T is a constant to be estimated, L is an arbitrarily large number, and the other terms are as previously defined. Note that the terms in the third argument of the Min function only apply to irrigated cotton production (i.e., IR = 1). The von Liebig function implies that yield responds in a linear fashion only to the limiting inputs (nitrogen fertilizer and irrigation) and that yield is not affected by the use of additional factors of production after reaching a given level. The specification imposes a zero elasticity of substitution implying that factor inputs are not substitutable for one another.

(d) Site Specific Variables

As noted previously, in addition to nitrogen fertilizer and irrigation, site specific characteristics can impact the yield of a crop. Therefore, to have a properly specified yield function, such factors must be reflected. Consequently, site specific variables are included in the yield function specifications to capture yield variations associated with site specific characteristics. Site variables are included in g such that

$$(4.5) \qquad g = b_0 + b_1\, IR + b_2\, WC + b_3\, SL + b_4\, PC + b_5\, RF + b_6\, SP + b_7\, OM$$

where IR is a variable indicating whether irrigation occurs (i.e., IR=1) or does not occur (i.e., IR=0),[1] WC is the water holding capacity of the soil, SL is the slope of the field, PC is a variable indicating whether the previous crop was cotton (i.e., PC=1) or some other crop (PC=0), RF is an index of the rainfall as defined by Wischmeier and Smith [1978], SP is a measure of the soil permeability, and OM is a measure of the organic matter content of the soil. Table 4.3 lists the variables used in the estimation and the units in which they are measured. Note that in defining the application timing of nitrogen fertilizer, the spring and the planting applications are combined into one variable, N_s. This is necessary due to the nuances of the way the relevant questions were asked on the Cotton Water Quality Survey.

Table 4.3. Ranges of Values for Each Variable Defined in the Model

Variable	Definition	Mean	Minimum	Maximum	Standard Deviation
Y (lbs/ac)	Yield	681	0	2880	412
WC (in/in)	Water Holding Capacity	0.16	0.03	0.26	0.043
SL (percentage)	Cropland Slope	0.013	0	0.1	0.014
SP (in /hr)	Soil permeability	2.24	0.06	13	2.9
W (ac-ft/ac)	Irrigation Rate	2.18	0	13	1.84
N_f (lbs/ac)	Fall Fertilizer	14	0	422	33
N_s (lbs/ac)	Spring Fertilizer	24	0	561	37
N_p (lbs/ac)	Fertilizer at Planting	4	0	172	16
N_g (lbs/ac)	Fertilizer at Growing	36	0	300	50
RF	R-factor	185	0	450	127
OM (mg)	Organic Matter	1.43	0.5	8	0.7

Finally, all of the data used in the estimation were obtained from the Cotton Water Quality Survey with the exception of the rainfall index, RF. Data used to construct this variable were obtained from the National Oceanic and Atmospheric Administration.

1 This implies that with irrigation, the production function shifts from what it would be with no irrigation.

EMPIRICAL RESULTS

(a) General Results

Before turning to the estimation of the various cotton yield functions, one caveat is in order. There is typically a problem of heteroscedasticity in cross section studies of the type being conducted here. This arises because of the large variation in the size of the entities for which data are obtained - cotton producers in the present instance. Consequently, in order to determine whether there are potential problems with the estimates (or more specifically, with the properties of the estimates which creates difficulties in using the estimates for inferential purposes), to test for the presence of heteroscedasticity, the approach suggested by White [1980] which was developed for the general linear model is used. Because only the quadratic specification of those being considered fits into the general linear model framework (it is a special case of the general linear model), only the results of the test performed on the quadratic yield function will be presented. As developed by White, the test statistic, based on the null hypothesis of homoscedasticity, is distributed as chi-square with the number of degrees of freedom equal to the product of the number of regressors and the number of regressors plus one divided by two. In the current example, the number of regressors equals 13 so the number of degrees of freedom equals 91. At the 5 percent level of significance, the critical value is 114.27. The value of the computed test statistic is 98.80 suggesting that the error terms in the quadratic yield function have a common variance. That is, the null hypothesis of homoscedasticity is accepted. This result permits avoiding the inferential pitfalls associated with heteroscedastic variances.

Nonlinear least squares was used to estimate the parameters for each cotton yield function specification. An examination of the matrix of correlation coefficients indicated no significant collinearity was present among the explanatory variables. Additionally, the variance-decomposition proportions (Belsley, Kuh, and Welsch [1980] are uniformly relatively small for the quadratic yield function. (The analysis is limited to the quadratic yield function for the same reason White's test for heteroscedasticity is applied only to the quadratic yield function.) The proportions never exceed 0.30 and typically average around 0.01 to 0.05. Table 4.4a, 4.4b, and 4.4c give the parameter estimates for the quadratic function, the Mitscherlich-Baule function, and the von Liebig function, respectively. Using the adjusted coefficient of determination (i.e., R^2) as an evaluation criterion, it appears that the quadratic specification, among those considered, best characterizes the relationship between factor inputs and cotton output (yield) with the von Liebig function being slightly behind in explanatory power. (Note that there are well known deficiencies associated with relying on this criterion when nonlinear models are being estimated. For a discussion of these shortcomings, see, e.g., Judge et al. [1985].)

Given the relative closeness in explanatory power of two of the functional specifications, a more objective test of the superiority of one over the other is warranted. To this end, a statistical test suggested by Davidson and MacKinnon [1981] will be employed.[2] Each of the functional specifications are compared pairwise with the others. The results of the Davidson-MacKinnon J-test strongly suggest that both the quadratic yield function and the von Liebig function are preferable to the Mitscherlich-Baule yield function specification.[3] When the quadratic yield function was compared to the von Liebig yield function, however, the results were inconclusive.[4] That is, one was not indicated to be preferable to the other. Given the results of this test, just the quadratic yield function and the von Liebig yield function will be used in assessing the nitrogen fertilizer use associated with the timing of application and irrigation.

The quadratic yield function indicates the presence of diminishing marginal returns with respect to the amount of nitrogen fertilizer applied and with respect to irrigation. Moreover, the results suggest that irrigation and nitrogen fertilizer use are complementary inputs. All of the signs on the terms involving nitrogen fertilizer application rates and associated with application timing and those associated with irrigation are consistent with *a priori* expectations. For example, an increase in the nitrogen fertilizer application rate in any period will result in an expansion in the cotton yield while an increase in irrigation likewise will yield an increase cotton output.

The von Liebig yield function, which assumes neither complementarity nor substitutability between nitrogen fertilizer use and irrigation, also has the expected signs on the estimated coefficients for nitrogen fertilizer use associated with application timing and irrigation. The signs and the orders of magnitude of the estimates on the variables in the von Liebig yield function, in general, are quite consistent with the estimates on the respective variables of the quadratic yield function.

---

2 Note that unlike some of the other tests considered in the preceding discussion, the Davidson-MacKinnon J-test is applicable to both nonlinear as well as linear functions.

3 The computed J-test statistic for comparing the Mitscherlich-Baule yield function to the quadratic yield function was 66.67. (The critical chi-square value at the 5 percent level is 3.84.) That is, when the null hypothesis was specified to be the Mitscherlich-Baule yield function and the alternative was specified to be the quadratic yield function, the null hypothesis was rejected. Alternatively, when the quadratic yield function (null hypothesis) was compared to the Mitscherlich-Baule yield function (alternative hypothesis), the computed test statistic was 1.72. The computed J-test statistic for the comparing the Mitscherlich-Baule yield function (null hypothesis) to the von Liebig yield function (alternative hypothesis) was 67.66. Alternatively, when von Liebig yield function (null hypothesis) was compared to the Mitscherlich-Baule yield function (alternative hypothesis), the computed test statistic was 3.24.

4 The computed J-test statistic for the comparing the von Liebig yield function to the quadratic yield function was 12.39. (The critical chi-square value at the 5 percent level is 3.84.) That is, when the null hypothesis was specified to be the von Liebig yield function and the alternative was specified to be the quadratic yield function, the null hypothesis was not rejected. On the other hand, when the quadratic yield function (null hypothesis) was compared to the von Liebig yield function (alternative hypothesis), the computed test statistic was 6.32 indicating that the null hypothesis could not be accepted.

Table 4.4a. Estimated Quadratic Cotton Yield Function[1]

$$Y = \underset{(63.21)}{315.20} + \underset{(39.43)}{118.58}\ IR + \underset{(319.47)}{186.83}\ WC - \underset{(691.11)}{1207.78}\ SL - \underset{(22.10)}{13.66}\ PC$$

$$+ \underset{(0.1203)}{0.1197}\ RF - \underset{(4.54)}{3.95}\ SP + \underset{(18.90)}{208.49}\ W - \underset{(2.52)}{22.12}\ W^2 - \underset{(14.03)}{16.47}\ OM$$

$$+ \underset{(0.3732)}{0.8779}\ W\ [N_f\ (\underset{(0.1920)}{0.5792} - \underset{(0.2142)}{0.2821}\ IR) + (N_s + N_p)\ (\underset{(0.1501)}{0.5920} - \underset{(0.1614)}{0.4041}\ IR)$$

$$+ N_g\ (1 - \underset{(0.1932)}{0.5763}\ IR)]$$

$$+ \underset{(0.8531)}{5.4724}\ [N_f\ (\underset{(0.1904)}{0.5790} - \underset{(0.2112)}{0.2828}\ IR) + (N_s + N_p)\ (\underset{(0.1515)}{0.5924} - \underset{(0.1604)}{0.4040}\ IR)$$

$$+ N_g\ (1 - \underset{(0.1930)}{0.5761}\ IR)]$$

$$- \underset{(0.8544)}{0.02373}\ [N_f\ (\underset{(0.1922)}{0.5792} - \underset{(0.2100)}{0.2824}\ IR) + (N_s + N_p)\ (\underset{(0.1514)}{0.5921} - \underset{(0.1661)}{0.4040}\ IR)$$

$$+ N_g\ (1 - \underset{(0.1931)}{0.5761}\ IR)]^2$$

Adjusted $R^2 = 0.5232$ MSE = 79960.0

[1] The values in parentheses are the standard errors of the estimates.

Table 4.4b. Estimated Mitscherlich-Baule Cotton Yield Function[1]

$$Y = (712.78 + 497.82\,IR + 339.85\,WC - 1352.32\,SL + 10.48\,PC - 0.2585\,RF$$
(109.22) (69.01) (445.45) (1026.11) (33.43) (0.2112)

$$- 8.95\,SP - 40.76\,OM)\,(1 - \exp(-0.0921\,(N_f\,(0.3343 + 0.4240\,IR)$$
(6.84) (19.33) (0.0411) (0.1431) (0.2700)

$$+ N_s\,(0.3219 + 0.6025\,IR) + N_g\,(1 + 2.50\,IR)))$$
(0.1551) (0.3903) (3.77)

$$(1 - (cxp(-1.8018\,W))\,IR)$$
(0.2002)

Adjusted $R^2 = 0.2802$ MSE = 120199.0

[1] The values in parentheses are the standard errors of the estimates.

Table 4.4c. Estimated Von Liebig Cotton Yield Function[1]

$$Y = 403.11\,IR + 154.46\,WC - 55.50\,SL - 39.21\,PC - 0.7464\,RF - 13.54\,SP$$
(32.02) (337.22) (72.66) (23.32) (0.1111) (4.71)

$$-30.56\,OM + Min\,(951.78, 475.56 + 12.41\,[N_f\,(0.3464 - 0.1774\,IR)$$
(14.13) (66.44) (65.35) (1.90) (0.0744) (0.0747)

$$+ N_s\,(0.3164 - 0.2097\,IR) + N_g\,(1 - 0.7758\,IR)], (248.65 + 4167.30\,W)\,IR$$
(0.0606) (0.0603) (0.0472) (92.51) (2217.20)

$$+ (1 - IR)\,2000)$$

Adjusted $R^2 = 0.4748$ MSE = 90017.0

[1] The values in parentheses are the standard errors of the estimates.

(b) Effects of Site Specific Variables on Cotton Yield

Before examining the effects of nitrogen fertilizer application timing and the extent of irrigation on yield and excess nitrogen in the soil, focus on just the impacts of site specific factors on cotton yield. To this end, consider first the impact of the presence or absence of irrigation. As expected, both functional specifications (i.e., the quadratic and the von Liebig) show that the irrigation variable is statistically significant at the 5% level indicating that irrigated cropland in general has a higher cotton yield than non-irrigated cropland. This is because irrigation promotes nutrient movement to the root by diffusion and mass flow (Rhoads [1984]).

The coefficient on water holding capacity is positive but not significantly different from zero at the 5% level for both functional specifications. A positive sign is anticipated on this variable suggesting that soil with a higher water holding capacity would produce a higher yield. This result is expected because the agronomy literature illustrates that a higher water holding capacity is linked to higher productivity (Metcalfe and Elkins [1980]). Also, a higher water holding capacity can increase nutrient concentration in the soil and enhance the rate of nutrient movement to the root by diffusion and mass flow (Rhoads [1984]).

The coefficient on the slope of the cropland variable is negative for both functions but not statistically significantly different from zero at the 5% level. A statistically significant negative sign was expected because a greater slope promotes nitrogen loss by surface runoff leaving less nitrogen fertilizer for plant uptake and a coincident reduction in yield (Gilliam and Hoyt [1987]).

A negative sign on the coefficient estimate for the previous crop planted variable indicates that a reduction in cotton yield would be realized if the previous planted crop were cotton. This result is expected because the continuous planting of cotton promotes the propagation of insect pests such as the boll weevil which causes a loss of cotton yield (Staten and Hinkle [1987] and Metcalfe and Elkins [1980]). Unfortunately, the coefficient estimate on this variable for both the quadratic yield function and the von Liebig function was not statistically significant at the 5% level.

The sign on the coefficient of the rainfall index variable should be negative because the index is designed to quantify the impact of rainfall on soil erosion (Wischmeier and Smith [1978]). A reduction in yield is associated with increased soil loss (Taylor and Frohberg [1978]). The estimate is statistically significant at the 5% level or better and has the correct sign only for the von Liebig cotton yield function.

The coefficient on soil permeability has a negative sign which is expected although it is statistically significant at the 5% level only for the von Liebig function. Soil with greater permeability has a larger potential for nitrate leaching thereby reducing the nitrogen available for plant uptake (Bock [1984]).

A relatively large amount of organic matter in the soil is often associated with elevated crop yields (Soil Conservation Service [1983]). Therefore, a positive sign is expected on the organic matter variable. The estimation results, however, yield negative signs although only the estimate on the von Liebig function is statistically significant at the 5% level. A further examination of this result is warranted in subsequent research.

(c) Impact of Irrigation on Cotton Yield

The impact of irrigation on cotton yield is statistically significant at the 5% level for the quadratic functional specification. The estimated coefficients on both the linear term and the quadratic term have the expected sign and are statistically significantly different than zero at the 5% level. The negative sign on the quadratic term indicates the presence of decreasing marginal returns with regard to the quantity of water applied.

In the von Liebig cotton yield function, irrigation has a positive effect but the coefficient on the linear term is not statistically significant at the 5% level. The statistical significance, however, of the coefficient on the IR term indicates that irrigation increases productivity overall. That is, irrigation has the effect of shifting the production function upward implying that, for example, the same soil will now yield a larger output all other things remaining the same except irrigation.

The interaction between the irrigation term and the amount of nitrogen fertilizer applied is positive and statistically significant at the 5% level in the quadratic model. This suggests that irrigation and nitrogen fertilizer use are complementary inputs. Irrigation serves to enhance nutrient movement in the root for plant use (Rhoads [1984]).

(d) Nitrogen Fertilizer Losses and the Timing of Application

To assess the nitrogen fertilizer losses associated with the timing of application, it is necessary to use the empirical estimates from the cotton yield functions. Nitrogen losses will be indicated by the proportion of nitrogen fertilizer applied but for which no increase in yield was observed. The estimation results indicate that for non-irrigated cotton, fall and spring applications losses are approximately the same as the amount lost during the growing period. For example, the quadratic specification shows that fall application losses are about 0.42 (1-0.58) for each pound of nitrogen fertilizer applied while the spring application losses are about 0.41 (1-0.59) for each pound of nitrogen fertilizer applied. The difference in nitrogen fertilizer losses associated with these two application timings is not statistically significantly different than zero at the 5% level. A similar conclusion is reached with regard to the von Liebig estimation results.

(e) Nitrogen Fertilizer Losses and Irrigation

Irrigation results in a significant loss of nitrogen fertilizer in cotton production. For example, the quadratic function estimation results indicate that, in the presence of irrigation, about 0.58 pounds of nitrogen fertilizer is lost for each pound of nitrogen fertilizer applied during the growing season. When spring application is used, 0.40 of each pound of nitrogen fertilizer applied is lost when irrigation is practiced relative to no such losses for the non-irrigated cotton production. Analogous results are obtained for the von Liebig functional specification.

It should be noted, however, that if nitrogen fertilizer is leached into the groundwater, some portion of the estimated loss may appear in the irrigation water and therefore be available for plant uptake. This is indicated by the complementary relation between nitrogen fertilizer applied and irrigation as shown by the statistically significant at the 5% level coefficient estimate on the nitrogen application/irrigation cross product term in the quadratic model. Also, some portion of the leached nitrogen fertilizer may contribute to the fertility of irrigated cropland. This is evinced by the statistically significant at the 5% level coefficient estimate on the irrigation variable, IR, in the specification. Unfortunately, given the way the information was collected on the Cotton Water Quality Survey, these effects cannot be separated from the estimated nitrogen fertilizer losses.

The combined timing and irrigation effects on nitrogen fertilizer losses show that spring nitrogen fertilizer application losses are no greater than the fall application losses. For example, the von Liebig model shows that for each pound of nitrogen fertilizer applied, the fall application will lose 0.85 (1 - (0.34 - 0.17)) pounds as compared with 0.89 (1- (0.31-0.20)) pounds for the spring application. Note that difference between these two values are not statistically significantly different than zero at the 5% level.

There are a variety of reasons why nitrogen fertilizer losses associated with a fall application should be different than the losses from a spring application. These include the fact that a relatively high carbon to nitrogen ratio during the fall favors immobilization of nitrates in the soil (Blackmer [1987]). Next, relatively high soil moisture content due to irrigation and spring rain leads to a relatively higher level of denitrification of newly applied nitrogen fertilizer. (Note that the denitrification process refers to the biological transformation of nitrogen in the nitrate or nitrite forms to gaseous forms that escape from the soil (Blackmer [1987]).) Finally, nitrogen fertilizer applied in the spring on the soil surface is more susceptible to runoff loss due rain, while nitrogen fertilizer applied in the fall is typically laid under the top soil. These factors suggest that the application timing between fall and spring should have differential effects on cotton production. The fact that the empirical results suggest that it does not will be the subject of a future investigation.

The regional implications of these results are uncomplicated. When individual states are compared with regard to the incidence the loss of nitrogen fertilizer due to a fall application versus a spring application, there is no statistical indication that fall application losses are greater in say, Texas, than they are in Tennessee. Likewise, there is no suggestion that spring application losses are higher in, say, New Mexico than they are in Louisiana. What this means is that a policy designed to restrict the fall and/or spring application of nitrogen fertilizer will not differentially impact the cotton farmers in one state versus those in another in terms of their nitrogen fertilizer application timing decisions.

THE EFFECT OF IRRIGATION ON EXCESS NITROGEN AND THE POTENTIAL FOR GROUNDWATER CONTAMINATION

As noted previously, excess nitrogen in the soil associated with the application of nitrogen fertilizer is a main cause of groundwater contamination. Alternatively, the interrelationship between irrigation and nitrogen fertilizer application and groundwater contamination is not so well delineated. The impact of irrigation on excess nitrogen can be either negative or positive. On the one hand, irrigation can exacerbate excess nitrogen losses through an increase in leaching. On the other hand, it can improve nitrogen use efficacy through the increase in productivity of cropland brought about by moving nitrogen into the root zone and facilitating its uptake by plants.

To illustrate these two effects, the previously introduced concept of excess nitrogen in the soil will be used. Recall that excess nitrogen in the soil, N_e, was defined as the amount of nitrogen fertilizer applied, N_a, in excess of the amount of nitrogen removed from the field at the end of the growing season. The amount of nitrogen removed is amount of nitrogen in the cotton lint and seeds harvested and in the cotton plant residues removed from the field after harvest. The relationship between excess nitrogen, N_e, the amount of nitrogen fertilizer applied, N_t, the amount of nitrogen fertilizer available for plant uptake, N_a, and crop yield, $Y(N_a, W, IR)$, can be expressed as

$$(4.6) \quad N_e = N_t - k\,Y(N_a, W, IR)$$

where k is the amount of nitrogen in one bale of cotton removed from the field assuming the plant residues are removed from the field after harvest in addition to the cotton lint and cotton seeds, W is the irrigation rate, and IR is a qualitative variable used to indicate whether cotton was irrigated or not. It is possible to explicitly derive the relationship between excess nitrogen and irrigation. This is accomplished in the Appendix to this chapter for the quadratic yield function. In like fashion, it can be computed for the Mitscherlich-Baule function and the von Liebig function.

For the quadratic yield function, irrigation will result in a reduction in excess nitrogen in the soil if

$$(4.7) \quad \{(b_1 + a_3 + 2\,a_4\,W + a_5\,N_a)\} - \{(a_1 + 2\,a_2\,N_a + a_5\,W)\,(N_f\,e_1 + N_s\,e_2 + N_g\,e_3)\} > 0.$$

Otherwise, irrigation will result in an increase in excess nitrogen in the soil. The terms in the first set of brackets represent the marginal yield gain due to increased nitrogen uptake by cotton plants while the term in the second set of brackets is the marginal yield loss due to nitrogen losses associated with nitrogen leaching out of the root zone. This relationship implies that the marginal gain in yield must outweigh the marginal loss in order to observe a reduction in excess nitrogen in the soil. As irrigation increases, the amount of excess nitrogen in the soil will increase.

What then is the maximum irrigation rate for which irrigation would promote a reduction of excess nitrogen in the soil? Relationship (4.7) (and implicitly the quadratic yield function) will be employed to compute this maximum irrigation rate. Irrigation below this maximum rate will promote a reduction in excess nitrogen associated with cotton production, while an irrigation rate above this maximum will exacerbate the excess nitrogen in the soil problem. Assume that a farmer applies 50 pounds of nitrogen fertilizer per acre in the spring and 50 pounds per acre during the growing season. The relevant values for relationship (4.7) from the quadratic yield function are: $b_1 = 118$, $a_1 = 5.47$, $a_2 = -0.0237$, $a_3 = 208.49$, $a_4 = -22.12$, $a_5 = 0.879$, $d_2 = 0.592$, $e_2 = -0.404$, and $e_3 = -0.579$. Using these values and solving for the irrigation rate, the optimal irrigation rate,

W*, is determined to be 2.13 acre-foot. Thus, as long as the irrigation rate is below 2.13 ac-ft per acre, irrigation should reduce excess nitrogen in the soil in cotton production. The average rate of irrigation was 2.18 acre-foot for the irrigated cotton producers surveyed (with a standard deviation of 1.84), it is concluded that irrigation on average had neither a positive nor a negative effect in reducing excess nitrogen in the soil associated with cotton production in the United States.

When individual states are considered, however, a somewhat different picture emerges. For example, both Arizona and California had nearly twice the maximum irrigation rate required to reduce excess nitrogen. Moreover, both of these states had above average rates of per-acre excess nitrogen fertilizer. To compound this problem, more than fifty percent of the population in each state relied on groundwater as their primary source of drinking water (Carey [1992]). On the other hand, other states including Georgia, North Carolina and Oklahoma had irrigation rates below the 2.13 ac-ft per acre rate so that irrigation results in a net reduction in excess nitrogen. Moreover, in these states, less than thirty five percent of the population relies on groundwater for their primary source of drinking water (Carey [1992]).

IMPLICATIONS

The regional implications of the application timing results are straightforward. When individual states are compared with regard to the incidence the loss of nitrogen fertilizer due to a fall application versus a spring application, there is no statistical indication that fall application losses are greater in one state versus another. Likewise, there is no suggestion that spring application losses are higher in one state relative to the other cotton producing states. What this means is that any policy designed to affect the application timing of nitrogen fertilizer will not in general differentially impact the cotton farmers in one state versus those in another.

With regard to irrigation, the implications for reducing excess nitrogen in the soil are clear. The potential for groundwater contamination due to the coincident application of nitrogen fertilizer and irrigation varies by state and a policy(ies) designed to reduce excess nitrogen in the soil must be tailored to those states where the potential is most serious. For example, Arizona where nearly ninety percent of the population relies on groundwater as its primary source of drinking water and where per acre excess nitrogen is 137 pounds per acre and where the irrigation rate approaches 4 ac-ft per acre needs to take steps to reduce significantly either or both the rate of application of nitrogen fertilizer and the rate of irrigation. Both of these actions, however, as the empirical results show will result in lower cotton yields. In other states such as North Carolina and Oklahoma, the potential appears to be minimal and no corrective measures are recommended.

CONCLUSIONS

For non-irrigated cotton, significantly more nitrogen fertilizer applied during the fall or the spring is lost relative to nitrogen fertilizer applied during the during the growing season. There is no evidence to suggest that the fall application of nitrogen fertilizer incurs a larger loss than that applied in the spring for either non-irrigated or irrigated cotton production. Irrigation practices result in significant nitrogen losses due to increased leaching. Irrigation does, however, reduce nitrogen loss by increasing plant uptake of nitrogen fertilizer. This result is indicated by the fact that the increase in cotton yield associated with irrigation exceeds the yield loss associated with an increase in nitrogen leaching due to irrigation.

At a regional level, the application timing results suggest that when individual states are compared with regard to the incidence of the loss of nitrogen fertilizer due to a fall versus a spring application, there is no indication that fall application losses are greater in one state versus another. Likewise, there is no suggestion that spring application losses are higher in one state relative to the other cotton producing states. What this means is that any policy designed to affect the application timing of nitrogen fertilizer will not in general differentially impact the decisions of cotton farmers in one state versus those in another.

Concerning the coincident application of nitrogen fertilizer and irrigation, the potential for groundwater contamination varies by state and a policy(ies) designed to reduce excess nitrogen in the soil must be targeted at those states where the potential is greatest. These policies can take a variety of forms including explicit limitations on the amount of nitrogen fertilizer that can be applied, inducements in the form of, say, payments to cover yield losses due to a reduced nitrogen fertilizer application rate, and/or a nitrogen fertilizer tax designed so that the cotton farmers internalize the externalities associated with the potential groundwater contamination due to excess nitrogen fertilizer application.

REFERENCES

Belsley, D., E. Kuh, and R. Welsch, *Regression Diagnostics*, John Wiley and Sons, Inc., New York, NY, 1980.

Blackmer, A., "Losses and Transport of Nitrogen from Soil," Chapter 5 in *Rural Groundwater Contamination*, F. D'itri and L. Wolfson, Lewis Publishers, Inc., Chelsea, MI, 1987.

Bock, B., "Efficient Use of Nitrogen in Cropping Systems," Chapter 18 in *Nitrogen in Crop Production*, American Society of Agronomy, Madison, WI, 1984.

Cantor, P., "Health Effects of Agrichemicals in Groundwater: What Do We Know?" *Agricultural Chemicals and Groundwater Protection: Emerging Management and Policy*, Proceedings of a Conference held at St. Paul, MN, October 22-23, 1988.

Carey, A., "Agriculture, Agricultural Chemicals, and Water Quality," in *Agriculture and the Environment*, U.S. Department of Agriculture, Washington, DC, 1992.

Central Platte Natural Resources District, *Groundwater Quality Improvement for the Central Platte Valley*, Central Platte Natural Resources District, Grand Island, NE, November 1989.

Cerrato, M. and A. Blackmer, "Comparison of Models for Describing Corn Yield Response to Nitrogen Fertilizer," *Agronomy Journal*, Vol 82 (1990), pp. 121-134.

Crutchfield, S., M. Ribaudo, P. Setia, D. Letson, and L. Hansen, *Cotton Production and Water Quality: An Initial Assessment*, Staff Report AGES 9105, Resources and Technology Division, Economic Research Service, U. S. Department of Agriculture, Washington, DC, January 1991.

Davidson, R., and J. MacKinnon, "Several Tests for Model Specification in the Presence of Alternative Hypotheses," *Econometrica*, Vol. 49 (1981), pp. 781-793.

Environmental Protection Agency, *National Survey of Pesticides in Drinking Water Wells: Phase I Report*, EPA 570/9-90-015, Environmental Protection Agency, Washington, DC, November 1990.

Fertilizer Institute, *The Fertilizer Handbook*, 2nd. ed., The Fertilizer Institute, Washington, DC, 1976.

Frank, M., B. Beattie and M. Embleton, "A Comparison of Alternative Crop Response Models," *American Journal of Agricultural Economics*, Vol 72 (1990), pp. 597-603.

Gilliam, J. and G. Hoyt, "Effect of Conservation Tillage on the Fate and Transport of Nitrogen," Chapter 13 in *Effects of Conservation Tillage on Groundwater Quality*, Lewis Publishers, Inc., Chelsea, MI, 1987.

Judge, G., W. Griffiths, R. Hill, H. Lutkepohl, and T. Lee, *The Theory and Practice of Econometrics*, 2nd. ed., John Wiley and Sons, Inc., New York, NY, 1985.

Kanwar, R., J. Baker, and D. Baker, "Tillage and Split N-Fertilizer Effects on Subsurface Drainage Water Quality and Crop Yields." *Transactions of the American Society of Agricultural Engineers*, Vol. 31 (1988), pp. 231-244.

Office of Technology Assessment, *Protecting the Nation's Groundwater From Contamination*, U.S. Government Printing Office, Washington, DC, 1984.

Nielsen, E. and L. Lee, *The Magnitude and Costs of Groundwater Contamination From Agricultural Chemicals: A National Perspective*, AER-576, Economic Research Service, U.S. Department of Agriculture, Washington, DC, October 1987.

Metcalfe, D. and D. Elkins, *Crop Production: Principles and Practices*, Fourth Edition, Macmillan Publishing Co., New York, NY, 1980.

Rhoads, F., "Nitrogen or Water Stress: Their Interrelationships," Chapter 20 in *Nitrogen in Crop Production*, American Society of Agronomy, Madison, WI, 1984.

Soil Conservation Service, *Application of Soil Information: Part 603*, 430-VI-NSH, Soil Conservation Service, U.S. Department of Agriculture, Washington, DC, 1983.

Stan, G. and Hinkle D, *Maintaining Cotton Yields through Fertilizer and Crop Rotations*, Bulletin 340, Agricultural Experiment Station, New Mexico College of Agriculture and Mechanic Arts, Albuquerque, NM, 1947.

Taylor, C. and K. Frohberg, "The Welfare Effects of Erosion Controls, Banning Pesticides, and Limiting Fertilizer Application in the Corn Belt: Reply, *American Journal of Agricultural Economics*, Vol 60 (1978), pp. 560-561.

Viets, F. and R. Hageman, *Factors Affecting the Accumulation of Nitrate in Soil, Water and Plants*, Agricultural Handbook No. 413, Agricultural Research Service, U.S. Department of Agriculture, Washington, DC, November 1971.

White, H., "A Heteroskedasticity-Consistent Covariance Matrix Estimator and a Direct Test for Heteroskedasticity," *Econometrica*, Vol. 48 (1980), pp. 817-838.

Wischemeier, W. and Smith D, *Predicting Rainfall Erosion Losses*, Agricultural Handbook Number 537, U.S. Department of Agriculture, Washington, DC, 1978.

CHAPTER 4 APPENDIX

Consider the following equations that were given in the text and with the variables as previously defined:

(1) $N_a = N_f (d_1 - e_1 IR) + N_s (d_2 - e_2 IR) + N_g (1 - e_3 IR)$

(2) $Y = \gamma + a_1 N_a + a_2 N_a^2 + a_3 W + a_4 W^2 + a_5 (W N_a) + e$

(5) $\gamma = b_0 + b_1 IR + b_2 WC + b_3 SL + b_4 PC + b_5 RF + b_6 SP + b_7 OM$

Excess nitrogen in the soil is defined as

(4A.1) $N_e = N_t - k E[Y(N_a, W, IR)]$

where k is amount of nitrogen in one bale of cotton and E is the expectation operator and N_t is the amount of nitrogen fertilizer applied. That is, $N_t = N_f + N_s + N_g$. A small change in N_e can be expressed as

(4A.2) $dN_e = - k (\partial Y/\partial N_a \, dN_a + \partial Y/\partial W \, dW + \partial Y/\partial IR \, dIR)$.

Recall that IR is a qualitative (0-1) variable. (The interpretation of its derivative will be provided below.) Substituting N_a and γ from equations (1) and (5), respectively, into the yield function (equation (2)) and taking the partial derivative of Y with respect to N_a, W and IR, respectively, equation (4A.2) can be expressed as

(4A.3) $dN_e = - k (b_1 dIR + (a_1 + 2 a_2 N_a + a_5 W) dN_a +$
$(a_3 + 2 a_4 W + a_5 N_a) dW)$.

The change in excess nitrogen due to irrigation is expressed as

(4A.4) $dN_e/dW = -k\,(b_1\,dIR/dW + (a_1 + 2\,a_2\,N_a + a_5\,W)\,dN_a/dW + (a_3 + 2\,a_4\,W + a_5\,N_a))$.

Next, taking the derivative of equation (1) with respect to W indicates that for a given nitrogen application rate, N_a,

(4A.5) $dN_a/dW = -\,(N_f\,e_1 + N_s\,e_2 + N_g\,e_3)\,dIR/dW$.

If it is assumed that dIR/dW = 1 (this is a valid assumption because IR is a qualitative variable and will not change with the irrigation rate), substitute dN_a/dW into equation (A.4) to obtain

(4A.6) $dN_e/dW = -k\,[b_1 - (a_1 + 2\,a_2\,N_a + a_5\,W)\,(N_f\,e_1 + N_s\,e_2 + N_g\,e_3) + (a_3 + 2\,a_4\,W + a_5\,N_a)]$

Whether irrigation will reduce or increase the excess nitrogen in the soil depends on the signs and relative magnitudes of the terms in the brackets in equation (4A.6). That is, irrigation will result in a reduction in excess nitrogen in the soil if

(4A.7) $(b_1 + a_3 + 2\,a_4\,W + a_5\,N_a) - (a_1 + 2\,a_2\,N_a + a_5\,W)\,(N_f\,e_1 + N_s\,e_2 + N_g\,e_3) > 0$.

Otherwise, irrigation will result in an increase in excess nitrogen in the soil.

Chapter 5

COSTS OF REDUCING RESIDUAL NITROGEN ON CROPLAND VULNERABLE TO NITRATE LEACHING

INTRODUCTION

Although limiting nitrogen use may be costly to regulate, there are various reasons to do so. For example, regulation is an effective tool to reduce nitrogen fertilizer use when the fertilizer price is very low relative to the commodity (output) price. It imposes the least explicit cost on a farmer compared with other approaches such as input or output taxes when the reduction of nitrogen fertilizer use is required (Huang and Lantin [1993]). It has been considered an effective tool to promote the adoption of farming practices that reduce nitrogen fertilizer use (Taylor and Swanson [1974]). Finally, it is the least-cost approach for society whose objective is to mitigate pollution problems associated with agricultural production such as nitrate leaching (Baumol and Oates [1988]).

The objective of this chapter is to evaluate the costs to a farmer of reducing nitrogen fertilizer use on cropland vulnerable to nitrate leaching. This information is especially useful for policy makers interested in providing an incentive to a farmer to reduce nitrate leaching (Heimlich [1995]).

The chapter is divided into four sections including a definition of residual nitrogen as a measure to limit nitrogen fertilizer use, the development of a dynamic model which incorporates nitrogen carry-over effects to determine the steady-state relationship among the application rate of nitrogen fertilizer and residual nitrogen available for potential leaching, an investigation of the effect of cropland's vulnerability on a farmer's compliance cost of reducing residual nitrogen, and the empirical estimation of the compliance cost associated with reducing nitrogen fertilizer application rates on cropland with a high leaching and moderate leaching potential. An Iowa case study is used as the basis for the empirical estimation.

DEFINING RESIDUAL NITROGEN

Residual nitrogen is used as a measure to limit nitrogen fertilizer use. It is defined as the difference between the amount of nitrogen applied from all sources on one acre of cropland and the amount of nitrogen that leaves one acre of cropland during the crop season. The amount of nitrogen applied to one acre of cropland includes nitrogen fertilizer applied by the farmer, a_t, and nitrogen credited from other sources, o_t, including previous legume crops, manure application, irrigation water, and inherent nitrogen.[1] The amount of nitrogen that leaves one acre of cropland is nitrogen in the crop, h_t, harvested at the end of the growing season.

An accurate estimate of the residual nitrogen available for leaching can be very difficult to obtain (Blackmer [1987]). For the purpose here, the per acre amount of residual nitrogen at time t, r_t, available for leaching is approximated by[2]

$$(5.1)\ r_t = a_t + o_t - h_t$$

It is assumed that the farmer is able to estimate the amount of nitrogen added, a_t and o_t, and the amount of nitrogen removed from the field, h_t, to calculate the level of residual nitrogen after harvest, r_t, using relationship (5.1). It is further assumed that for the areas where soil conditions favor water infiltration, reducing the residual nitrogen that is available for potential leaching, r_t, is tantamount to reducing nitrogen leaching into the groundwater. For the other areas, it is assumed that the residual nitrogen can be lost not only through leaching, but also by denitrification, volatilization, water run-off and soil erosion, or remain in the soil at the end of crop season. The residual nitrogen as defined by equation (5.1) will be used as the benchmark to quantify the nitrogen available for potential leaching associated with a crop production practice. Using residual nitrogen as a measure, a dynamic model based on a nitrogen mass balance framework (Meisinger [1984] and Schaffer et al. [1990]) is used to determine the relationship between the level of residual nitrogen and the level of nitrate leaching at a steady-state condition. The steady-state solutions are used to investigate the effect of cropland's leaching potential on the cost of compliance.

---

1 The inherent nitrogen of a specific field is defined as the amount of nitrogen in harvested crops from the field without application of nitrogen fertilizer estimated from long-term yields (Voss and Shrader [1988]). This consists mainly of nitrogen from soil and precipitation.

2 Equation (5.1) is used mainly to define the amount of residual nitrogen available for potential leaching. It is not a nitrogen balance equation. A general nitrogen balance equation is given by (Meisinger [1984]): N-input - N-output equals the change in N-storage. N-input includes nitrogen from all sources, N-output includes all nitrogen that leaves the field, and change in N-storage includes the change in soil organic-N content and the change in soil inorganic-N content.

A Dynamic Model for Determining Optimal Nitrogen Fertilizer Application Rates

A farm-level dynamic programming model that maximizes expected present value of net farm income subject to a system of nitrogen mass balance equations is developed. The technical foundation of the model follows the formulation of Taylor [1983] and Kennedy [1986]. Assumed is the existence of a stochastic yield function, a stochastic carry-over function, and output price uncertainty. Given expected crop price $p^y{}_t$, fertilizer price $p^f{}_t$, stochastic yield $Y_t(n_t,d_t)$, where d_t is a random variable, and annual fixed cost fc, the expected per acre net farm income at time t subject to time discount a is formulated as[3]

$$(5.2) \quad z_t = E[\alpha\, p^y{}_t\, Y_t(n_t,\delta_t) - p^f{}_t\, \alpha_t - fc]\, \alpha^{t-1}.$$

This is subject to a nitrogen mass balance described by

$$(5.3) \quad n_t = a_t + x_t$$

$$(5.4) \quad r_t = a_t - v\, Y_t(n_t,\delta_t)$$

$$(5.5) \quad x_{t+1} = (1-K_t(w_t,\varepsilon_t))\,(x_t + r_t)$$

$$(5.6) \quad \theta_t = K_t(w_t,\varepsilon_t)\,(x_t + r_t)$$

$$(5.7) \quad 0 \leq x_t \leq r^m$$

Equation (5.3) states that nitrogen available for plant uptake, n_t, is the amount of applied nitrogen, a_t, plus carry-over nitrogen, x_t (Schaffer et al. [1990] and Williams et al. [1990]). Equation (5.4) redefines the residual nitrogen (equation (5.1)) as the difference between nitrogen applied and nitrogen removed with the harvested crop, $v\ Y_t(n_t,\delta_t)$, where v is the amount of nitrogen in one unit of harvested crop (Meisinger [1984]). Equation (5.5) is a stochastic carry-over function which states that the amount of carry-over nitrogen expected in time period t+1 is determined by the amount of nitrogen available for potential leaching $(x_t + r_t)$, and the fraction, $(1-K_t(w_t,\varepsilon_t))$, carried over. The percentage of nitrogen available for potential leaching from cropland, $K_t(w_t,\varepsilon_t)$, is determined by w_t, which reflects weather and site-specific variables such as precipitation and soil type, and by ε_t a random variable (Schaffer et al. [1990] and Williams and Krissel [1990]). Equation (5.6) calculates the amount nitrogen leached (Schaffer et al. [1990]). Equation (5.7) sets the maximum level of nitrogen carry-over, r^m, that can be stored in the soil. The value of k_t approaches 1 for cropland highly vulnerable to nitrate leaching, while the value of k_t approaches 0 for cropland not vulnerable to nitrate leaching.

For a profit-maximizing farmer facing a stochastic crop response (yield) function, a stochastic carry-over function, and uncertainty in the crop price, the problem of

---

3 A general discussion of the solution for this type of discrete time model is provided by Takayama [1988].

determining the nitrogen fertilizer application rate to maximize expected net farm income, z_t, over time is given as

(5.8)

$$Max_{a_1 \ldots a_m} \sum_{t=1}^{m} \alpha^{t-1} E[\alpha P_t^y Y_t(n_t,\delta_t) - p_t^f a_t]$$

subject to

$$a_t \geq 0$$
$$n_t = x_t + a_t$$
$$x_{t+1} = (1 - K_t(w_t,\varepsilon_t))(x_t + a_t - \nu Y_t(n_t,\delta_t))$$

with

$$x_1 \text{ given}$$

The problem can be reformulated as a dynamic programming optimization problem (Taylor [1983] and Kennedy [1986]). This reformulation is given as

(5.9)

$$\zeta_t\{x_t\} = \text{Max}_{a_t} E[\alpha p_t^y Y_t(n_t,\delta_t) - p_t^f a_t + \alpha \zeta_{t+1}\{x_{t+1}\}] \text{for } t = 1,2,\ldots,m$$

subject to

$$n_t = x_t + a_t$$
$$x_{t+1} = (1 - K_t(w_t,\varepsilon_t))(x_t + a_t - \nu Y_t(n_t,\delta_t))$$
$$a_t \geq 0$$

with

$$x_1 \text{ given}$$
$$\zeta_{m+1}\{x_{m+1}\} = 0$$

By assuming the random variables d_t and e_t are independent and the determination of p^f_{t+1} is conditional on p^f_t, the solution of this dynamic programming problem gives the rule for optimal nitrogen fertilizer application rate. The derivation is given in the Appendix to Chapter 5. The rule for determining the optimal application rate is

(5.10)

$$\alpha E[\, p_t^y \,]\partial\, E\,[\, Y_t(n_t,\delta_t\,)]/\partial\, a_t =$$
$$p_t^f - \alpha(1 - E\,[\, K_t(\, w_t,\varepsilon_t\,)])(1 - v\partial\, E\,[\, Y_t(\, n_t,\delta_t\,)]/\partial\, a_t\,)\, E\,[\, p_{t+1}^f \mid p_t^f\,]$$

Equation (5.10) equates the expected value of the marginal product of nitrogen fertilizer to the nitrogen fertilizer price less the discounted expected marginal value of carry-over nitrogen.

Equation (5.10) is a certainty equivalence formulation for the determination of the optimal nitrogen fertilizer application when both yield and carry-over nitrogen are subject to random variation (Taylor [1984]). Because it is a deterministic equation, the determination of an optimal nitrogen fertilizer application rate is simple. Assuming the current nitrogen price, p^f_t, is known at the time of the nitrogen fertilizer use decision, the optimal amount of nitrogen available for plant uptake in time period t, n^*_t, can be determined by knowing only the initial carry-over nitrogen level in the soil, x_t, the expected crop price, $E[p^y_t]$, the expected leaching rate, $E[(K_t(w_t,\varepsilon_t)]$, and the expected nitrogen fertilizer price in the next time period, $E[p^f_{t+1}|p^f_t]$. The optimal nitrogen application rate for time period t, a^*_t, is just the difference between n^*_t and x_t. Moreover, the amount of nitrogen carried-over from time period t to time period t+1, x_{t+1}, can be determined by equation (5.5). Carry-over nitrogen, x_{t+1}, becomes the carry-over nitrogen value for determining the optimal nitrogen application rate for time period t+1. Using this procedure the optimal nitrogen fertilizer application rate for future time periods can be obtained. When these optimal nitrogen application rates become temporally identical, a steady-state nitrogen application rate has been reached. The existence of steady-state solutions and use these steady-state solutions to estimate the cost of reducing nitrogen fertilizer use are developed in the next section.

STEADY-STATE SOLUTIONS

The steady-state solutions from using rule (5.10) can be determined by assuming a constant price for nitrogen fertilizer, a constant price for the crop, an expected (average) leaching percentage, and an expected (average) yield function. A steady-state solution is obtained when the solution of a dynamic problem remains unchanged through time. Two steady-state solutions - a steady-state solution where no limit is placed on nitrogen fertilizer use and a steady-state solution where nitrogen fertilizer use is constrained - are determined.

Without a restriction on nitrogen fertilizer use, it can be shown that a steady-state solution exits by solving the dynamic rule (5.10) recursively. The steady-state optimal nitrogen level for plant uptake, n^* (subscript t is dropped to indicate the steady-state solution), and the steady-state optimal nitrogen application rate, a^*, can be obtained in two time periods. In the first time period, an arbitrary initial value x_0 is assigned, and relationship (5.10) is solved to obtain the steady-state value, n^*. Subsequently, the expected steady-state optimal yield, $E[Y_t(n^*,\delta_t)]$ is computed. In the second time period, the amount of carry-over nitrogen, x_1, is computed. This will be the initial value for the second time period. The value of $x_1 = (1-E[K_t(w_t,\varepsilon_t)])\ (n^* - v\ E[Y_t(n^*,\delta_t)])$ from equations (5.3), (5.4) and (5.5). This value of x_1 is the steady-state value, x^*. The steady-state optimal application rate, a^*, is then obtained by subtracting x^* from n^*. It can be expressed as[4]

$$(5.11)\ a^* = \{E[K_t(w_t, \varepsilon_t)] / (1 - E[K_t(w_t, \varepsilon_t)])\}\ x^* + v\ E[Y_t(n^*,\delta_t)].$$

With a restriction on the residual nitrogen reduced to r^0, the steady-state level of carry-over nitrogen in the soil, x^0, the amount of nitrogen fertilizer to be applied, a^0, and the steady-state level of nitrogen available for potential leaching, θ^0, can be obtained in two steps. First, for a given r^0, the steady-state carry-over nitrogen x^0 can be determined by solving x_t from the relationship

$$(5.12)\ x_t = (1-E[K_t(w_t,\varepsilon_t)])\ (x_t + r^0) \text{ for all t.}$$

Since r^0 is a constant, the steady-state level of carry-over nitrogen is

$$(5.13)\ x^0 = [(1-E[K_t(w_t, \varepsilon_t)])/E[K_t(w_t, \varepsilon_t)]]\ r^0.$$

Relationship (5.13) states that the steady-state level of carry-over nitrogen, x^0, is determined by the expected (average) leaching percentage and the fixed amount of reduced residual nitrogen applied, r^0, regardless of the initial level of carry-over nitrogen in soil. Second, the steady-state nitrogen application rate, a^0, corresponding to a given r^0, can be obtained by solving equation (5.4). A unique value for a^0 can usually be obtained because the yield function typically exhibits diminishing marginal returns.

Substituting r^0 for r_t and x^0 of equation (5.13) for x_t in equation (5.5), the steady-state level of nitrate leaching is

---

4 The steady-state application rate, without limiting nitrogen use, can be derived directly from the carry-over function (5.5) and residual nitrogen relationship (5.4). When a steady-state is reached, the carry-over function becomes $x^* = (1- E[K_t(w_t,\varepsilon_t)])\ (x^* + r^*)$. Substituting r^* by $(a^* - v\ E[Y(n^*,\delta_t))$ and rearranging the carry-over function, the steady-state application rate can be obtained as $a^* = \{E[K_t(w_t,\varepsilon_t)]/(1 - E[K_t(w_t,\varepsilon_t)])\}\ x^* + v\ E[Y(n^*,\delta_t)]$ where n^* is obtained from condition (5.10), and then is used to compute x^* for calculating a^*.

$$(5.14)\ \theta^0 = r^0 .$$

Relationship (5.14) states that when a steady-state is reached, the amount of residual nitrogen applied determines the amount of nitrate leaching. This relationship also applies when there is no fertilizer use restriction.[5]

COMPLIANCE COST OF LIMITS ON FERTILIZER USE ON VULNERABLE CROPLAND

In the previous section, it was shown that steady-state solutions could be obtained for situations when the nitrogen application rate is not restricted and when the nitrogen fertilizer application rate is restricted. Next, using these two steady-state solutions, the issue of whether limiting residual nitrogen fertilizer will impose a higher cost on those farmers with high-leaching cropland than those farmers with low-leaching cropland is investigated. Let $z^*(k)$ and $z^0(k)$, where $k=E[k_t(w_t,\varepsilon_t)]$, be the expected steady-state annual net returns from crop production without and with limits on nitrogen fertilizer use. Assume all other parameters in equation (5.2) are the same. The compliance cost, c(k), can then be defined as

$$(5.15)\ c(k) = z^*(k) - z^0(k)$$

where

$$(5.16)\ z^*(k) = p^y\, y(n^*) - p^f\, a^* - fc$$

and

$$(5.17)\ z^0(k) = p^y\, y(n^0) - p^f\, a^0 - fc$$

where p^y and p^f are constant prices of the crop and fertilizer and no time discount is assumed (a = 1), and y is the expected yield, $E[Y_t(n,\delta_t)]$. The partial derivative of equation (5.15) with respect to k is

(5.18) < 0 (> 0), an increase in the expected leaching rate k will reduce (increase) compliance cost when a nitrogen fertilizer use restriction is imposed. Using the relationship $n^* = a^* + [(1-k)/k]\ r^*$ at the steady-state derived from equations (5.3) and (5.13), the partial derivative of equation (5.16) with respect to k is

[5] Moreover, if it is desirable to restrict the nitrogen application rate in order to maintain an optimal level of carry-over nitrogen, x^o, in the soil, the application rate can be obtained in two steps. First, compute the steady-state level of residual nitrogen, r^o, using the relationship $r^o = E[k]/(1-E[k])\ x^o$. Second, with x^o and r^o given, equation (5.4) can be solved to obtain a^o.

(5.19) $\partial z^*(k)/\partial k = - p^y (\partial y/\partial n^*) (1/k^2) r^*$.

Similarly, the partial derivative of equation (5.17) with respective to k can be expressed as

(5.20) $\partial z^0(k)/\partial k= - p^y (\partial y/\partial n^0) (1/k^2) r^0$.

Since $p^y > 0$, $\partial y/\partial n^* \geq 0$, $r^* \geq 0$, and $k > 0$, the derivatives satisfy

(5.21) $\partial z^*(k)/\partial k \leq 0$ and $\partial z^*(k)/\partial k \leq 0$.

The implication is that net farm income will decrease as the rate of nitrate leaching, k, increases. It is not clear, however, whether compliance cost will decrease as k increases.

Substituting equations (5.19) and (5.20) into equation (5.18), one obtains

(5.22) $\partial c(k)/\partial k = [- p^y (\partial y/\partial n^*) (1/k^2) r^*] + [p^y (\partial y/\partial n^0) (1/k^2) r^0]$

By assuming that the marginal physical product (MPP) of nitrogen is diminishing, the MPP under a restriction on nitrogen fertilizer use is greater than the MPP without restriction. That is, $p^y (\partial y/\partial n^*) < p^y (\partial y/\partial n^0)$. However, since $r^* > r^0$, the sign of the value on the right-hand-side of equation (5.22) is indeterminate. Thus, whether the compliance cost is higher or lower for high-leaching-potential cropland than for low-leaching-potential cropland cannot be theoretically determined. It is an empirical issue. An Iowa case study is used in the next section to determine the compliance cost with respect to the magnitude of nitrogen leaching.

OPTIONS TO REDUCE NITROGEN FERTILIZER USE

The case study allowed profit-maximizing farmers to plant corn continuously with a reduced nitrogen fertilizer use or to plant corn in rotation with other crops to reduce nitrogen fertilizer use. The crop rotations considered were soybeans-corn, and oats-meadow-corn. These are the common rotations in Iowa (Gill and Daberkow [1991]). The analysis focuses on crop rotations for corn production because corn uses large amounts of nitrogen fertilizer. The continuous planting of corn uses nitrogen fertilizer inefficiently[6] and is potentially the source of a large amount of nitrate leaching into the groundwater.

The farm-level performance of various crop rotations under four different options is considered in order to evaluate the compliance cost when limits on nitrogen fertilizer use are imposed. The four options are (a) no restriction on nitrogen fertilizer use, (b)

6 The Iowa State University field experiment data (Voss and Shrader [1988]) indicate a relatively large quantity of residual nitrogen.

continuous planting of corn with a restriction, (c) soybean-corn rotation with a restriction, and (d) oat/meadow-meadow-corn rotation with a restriction.

(a) No Restriction on Nitrogen Fertilizer Use

Under this option cropland targeted for a reduction in the nitrogen fertilizer application rate is assumed to be in the farm program. No restriction on the nitrogen fertilizer application rate is imposed on crop rotations and nitrogen credits are considered for growing legume crops prior to planting corn. This option is used as the benchmark for comparison of the different crop rotation patterns under a restriction on nitrogen fertilizer use.

(b) Continuous Planting of Corn with a Restriction on Nitrogen Fertilizer Use

The farmer continuously planting corn (i.e., planting corn from one growing season to the next) under this option will be allowed to participate in the farm program but he or she is required to reduce the nitrogen fertilizer application rate. An arbitrary standard of zero residual nitrogen ($r_t = 0$) available for potential leaching as defined by relationship (5.4) is imposed.

(c) Soybeans-Corn Rotation with a Restriction on Nitrogen Fertilizer Use

The farmer growing soybeans and corn in rotation will be allowed to participate in the farm program under this option but he or she will be required to reduce the nitrogen fertilizer application rate so that the residual nitrogen available for potential leaching is equal to zero. There will be a credit for nitrogen fixed by soybeans.

(d) Oat/Meadow-Meadow-Corn Rotation with a Restriction on Nitrogen Fertilizer Use

Under this option, the farmer growing oat/meadow, meadow and corn in a three-year rotation[7] will be allowed to participate in the farm program but he or she will be required to reduce the nitrogen fertilizer application rate so that the residual nitrogen available for potential leaching is equal to zero. There will be a credit for nitrogen fixed by the meadow, a legume crop.

---

[7] The oats-meadow, meadow, and corn rotation is a common way to produce alfalfa in Iowa. Farmers plant alfalfa-grass seed with oats as companion crop in the first year of rotation. In the second year, they grow alfalfa and then plant corn in the third year.

DATA AND ASSUMPTIONS

Experimental data from an Iowa State University research farm study at Kanawha, Iowa (Iowa State Experiment Station [1986] and Voss and Shrader [1988]) were used to estimate expected yield responses to nitrogen fertilizer applications.[8]

The Iowa study examined the effects of nitrogen fertilizer application rates and crop rotation patterns on crop yields. In the study only the nitrogen fertilizer application rate and the sequence of crop rotations varied. All other factors were held constant. In each rotation, only corn production received nitrogen fertilizer. Four nitrogen fertilizer application rates (0, 80, 160 and 240 pounds per acre) were used on replicative plots of each crop rotation over 25 years. The average corn yield data from the 1984-1987 time period were used to estimate the expected corn yield functions for specific crop rotations. Soybeans and the first-year and the second-year meadow yield levels were kept constant regardless of the amount of nitrogen applied on the preceding corn crop in the rotation. Experimental data substantiate the validity of this assumption (Voss and Shrader [1988]).

The Iowa experiment data are used to estimate the expected yield function which relates yield responses, $y(n_t)$, to the amount of nitrogen available for plant uptake, n_t, which includes the applied nitrogen fertilizer, a_t, and the carry-over nitrogen x_t. Since the carry-over nitrogen was not directly measured in the Iowa field experiments, it must be estimated. To estimate x_t requires the assumption that the experiment data are collected in a steady-state.[9] With this assumption, a value for the steady-state carry-over nitrogen can be computed.[10]

The plateau production function of a Mitscherlich type was used to estimate the expected steady-state yield functions because it is a good interpreter of experimental data (Paris [1992] and Frank et al. [1990]). The estimated expected yield functions for corn

---

8 One must use actual farm field data to estimate actual yield response to nitrogen fertilizer use if the analysis is intended for policy purposes. In Iowa the efficiency of nitrogen fertilizer use generally is comparable between the experimental field and the farm field in the region where the experiment station is located.

9 It is assumed that the average yields obtained from the replicative field plots where fixed amounts of nitrogen fertilizer were applied continuously over a four-year period approximate the yield steady-state. The steady-state assumption is justified because if a fixed amount of nitrogen fertilizer is applied every year to a plot, the yield level from a plot will reach a steady-state. The amount of nitrogen available for plant uptake also will reach a steady-state. Prior to the four-year period, each of the plots received the same amount of nitrogen for more than twenty years.

10 The steady-state value of the carry-over nitrogen for each experiment observation is obtained by solving x' from the steady-state equation $a' = K / (1 - K)\, x' + v\, y'$, where a' is the nitrogen fertilizer application rate, v is assumed to be 0.9, y is the yield response to the nitrogen fertilizer application, and K is the leaching rate. It is assumed that K is 0.3. This assumed leaching rate generally is applicable for the cropland in the Cornbelt region (Aldrich [1984] and Blackmer [1987]). The value of y' was regressed on $(a' + x')$ to estimate the yield function $Y(n')$ for the model. A value of $K = 0.5$ was also considered. In this instance, the estimated parameters in the yield function changed relatively little.

under three different crop sequences are given in Table 5.1. The intercept of the yield function for the continuous planting of corn is the annual corn yield that would be realized from the soil without the application of any nitrogen fertilizer. It can be used as the measure of the productivity associated with the inherent nitrogen in the soil (Voss and Shrader [1988]). The yield corresponding to a specific nitrogen application rate, a', shown in the yield function is the result of nitrogen contribution from three sources - the nitrogen fertilizer applied, a', the steady-state carry-over nitrogen induced by a', and the inherent nitrogen.

Table 5.1. Estimated Coefficients for An Expected Steady-State Corn Yield Function in Response to Nitrogen Fertilizer Application Rates for Different Preceding Crops[1]

Rotations	A(i,j)	B(i,j)	C(i,j)	R^2
Corn after Corn	153.15	0.0102	53.807	0.94
	(8.705)	(0.0027)	(13.052)	
Sample size = 16				
Corn after Soybeans	167.01	0.0114	90.018	0.95
	(5.776)	(0.0032)	(22.33)	
Sample Size = 8				
Corn after Meadow	168.3	0.0104	214.975	0.78
	(3.17)	(0.0091)	(169.53)	
Samplc Sizc = 8				

[1] The expected steady-state yield function is specified as y(i,j) = A(i,j)*{1 - Exp[-B(i,j)(C(i,j) + n(i,j))]}, where y(i,j) denotes the yield for crop i preceded by crop j, n(i,j) is the nitrogen available for plant uptake, including nitrogen fertilizer applied and carry-over nitrogen for crop i when preceded by crop j, and A(i,j), B(i,j) and C(i,j) are coefficients to be estimated. Only corn received nitrogen fertilizer applications. Note that the values in parentheses are standard errors of the estimates.

The expected steady-state yield functions for corn in rotation with legume crops relates the yield response to the fixed amounts of nitrogen fertilizer applied because the effect of carry-over fertilizer nitrogen applied in corn production in the previous year is insignificant. This is mainly due to the fact that legume crops absorb all the carry-over nitrogen from previous applications in corn production and their yields are constant regardless of the level of carry-over nitrogen. The difference between the intercept when corn is continuously planted without nitrogen fertilizer application and the intercepts when one of the legume-corn rotation sequences is planted is assumed to be the yield response attributable to the legume-fixed nitrogen used subsequently by corn.

Each crop sequence under each of the options is examined for cropland with a high potential for leaching (i.e., k=1) and for cropland with a moderate leaching potential (i.e., k=0.5). For the purpose of exposition, an average value, k, for k_t across time periods is assumed. For the high-leaching cropland, it is assumed that for each time period, t, any unused nitrogen will be lost and hence cannot be used for future (i.e., t+1, t+2, ...) crop production. For the moderate leaching cropland, it is assumed that 50 percent of the residual nitrogen plus applied nitrogen is carried over from one period to the next. The internal nitrogen requirement of 0.9 is used for ensuring the amount of nitrogen applied is removed from the field. The initial level of nitrogen in the soil, x_1, is calculated from the inherent yield (intercept of yield function) by assuming the farmer is continuously planting corn with no application of nitrogen fertilizer.

Cost of production data are estimated by Duffy and Judd [1991]. The cost data represent average production costs for farms in Iowa. The commodity price data are from the Economic Research Service [September 1990]). The weighted average 1991 nitrogen fertilizer price ($0.20 per pound) (Vroomen and Taylor [1992]) is assumed to prevail initially, although a sensitivity analysis is conducted in order to examine the effects of variations in the price of nitrogen fertilizer on the results. Five percent (a=0.05) of corn base acreage is assumed in the Acreage Reduction Program (ARP) and 15 percent (b=0.15) of the corn base acreage is flexed acres (U.S. Congress [1990]). All flexed acres are assumed planted with corn under the continuous planting of corn. The expected annual net farm income z_t (equation (5.2)) is modified to reflect these assumptions. For example, the expected annual net return for the continuous corn rotation is reformulated as

$$(5.23)\quad z_t = \alpha^{t-1} E[\{(1\text{-}a\text{-}b)[a\, p^y_t\, Y(n_t,\delta_t) + D - p^f_t\, \alpha_t - fc]] + b\, [\alpha\, p^y_t\, Y(n_t,\delta_t) + - p^f_t\, \alpha_t - fc]\,\}$$

where D in equation (5.23) is the deficiency payment which is the product of program yield, y_p, and the maximum value of either the market price or the loan rate. Inclusion of the deficiency payment in the net farm income is needed to assess the income effect from a change in crop rotation to reduce nitrogen fertilizer use. The steady-state solution for each crop rotation under each option is obtained.

SIMULATION RESULTS

(a) No Fertilizer Use Restriction

Regardless of the leaching potential of the cropland, switching from the continuous planting of corn to an oats-meadow-corn rotation while having no fertilizer use restrictions will reduce the residual nitrogen available for potential leaching and net farm income. It will not, however, eliminate the residual nitrogen as defined by equation (5.1) on cropland with either a high or moderate leaching potential. A relatively large amount of nitrogen fertilizer is required for the production of corn. Nitrogen fixed by the meadow alone will not be sufficient to produce corn so that the maximum net farm income will not be realized. The results show that when fertilizer is priced at $0.20 per pound, the oats-meadow-corn rotation needs an additional 104 pounds of nitrogen fertilizer per acre to grow corn optimally in addition to the nitrogen fixed by the meadow on moderate leaching cropland. If the nitrogen applied in the form of fertilizer and that fixed by the meadow are considered in concert, the oats-meadow-corn rotation still shows that there is some residual nitrogen available for leaching on cropland with either a high or a moderate leaching potential. The results show that the oats-meadow-corn rotation will have 37 pounds of residual nitrogen per acre potentially available for leaching in moderate leaching cropland.

Furthermore, switching from the continuous planting of corn to a soybeans-corn rotation will cause a larger reduction in nitrogen fertilizer use and, hence, residual nitrogen. There will be a smaller reduction in net farm income on cropland with a moderate leaching potential but a small increase in net farm income on cropland with a high leaching potential. The simulation results suggests that the reduction in nitrogen fertilizer use is 49 pounds on cropland with a high leaching potential compared to a reduction of 27 pounds on cropland with a moderate leaching potential. The decrease in net farm income is expected to be \$5 per acre on cropland with a moderate leaching potential and the increase in net farm income is \$4 per acre for cropland with a high leaching potential. These results clearly indicate that a policy aimed at reducing excess nitrogen fertilizer use would be cost effective if it is targeted at cropland with a high leaching potential.

(b) Limiting Fertilizer Use

Next, consider the impact on a profit-maximizing farmer when nitrogen fertilizer use is restricted. In this case, a constraint of zero residual nitrogen ($r_t = 0$) is imposed on equation (5.4). While the price of corn is assumed to be, as before, \$2.35 per bushel, it is now assumed that the price of nitrogen fertilizer ranges between \$0.10 and \$0.30 per pound in \$0.10 increments. This assumption will determine how sensitive the results are to the price of nitrogen fertilizer. As before each rotation is examined based on cropland with either a high or moderate leaching potential. The effects on the fertilizer application rates and net farm income of limiting fertilizer use are shown in Table 5.2a and Table 5.2b, respectively. The results show a significant reduction in the nitrogen fertilizer application rate for each of the planting options considered including the continuous planting of corn, a soybeans-corn rotation, and a oats-meadow-corn rotation when zero residual nitrogen potential for leaching is imposed.[11] The results also show no difference in the nitrogen fertilizer application rate for the nitrogen fertilizer prices assumed between the two types of cropland. This result is not surprising because within the range of nitrogen fertilizer prices assumed, imposing a constraint on fertilizer use forces residual nitrogen to equal zero (i.e., r_t in equation (5.4) is set to zero) at each time period

[11] When residual nitrogen equals zero, the amount of nitrogen applied is equal to the amount of nitrogen removed from the harvested crop. In this Iowa study, the nitrogen in the harvested crop includes nitrogen fertilizer applied plus inherent nitrogen.

and therefore the nitrogen application rates are the same.[12] Furthermore, when fertilizer use is limited, the soybeans-corn rotation will provide the highest net farm income followed by continuous planting of corn. The farmer who continuously plants corn would be better off by switching to the soybeans-corn rotation.

(c) Compliance Cost

Finally, the farmer is inherently concerned with the effect on net farm income of adopting different crop rotations to reduce nitrogen fertilizer use. This effect can be computed simply as the difference in net farm income from the continuous planting of corn assuming that this is the practice initially employed by the farmer and the planting under a soybeans-corn or meadow-corn rotation. The compliance cost for the three different cropping schemes were computed by assuming that the farmer plants his or her crops first on land with a high potential for leaching and second on land with a moderate potential for leaching. The results are presented in Table 5.3a. They show that when the nitrogen fertilizer price is relatively low, a fertilizer use restriction on cropland that is highly vulnerable to potential leaching will have a slightly smaller compliance cost relative to cropland with a moderate leaching potential. The compliance cost on both types of cropland decreases as the price of nitrogen fertilizer increases. The soybeans-corn rotation with a restriction on fertilizer use has the lowest compliance cost. In fact this compliance cost becomes negative (i.e., the net farm income under the soybeans-corn rotation actually exceeds the net farm income from the continuous planting of corn) for a price of nitrogen fertilizer exceeding $0.30 per pound.

The effect on net farm income of a change in nitrogen fertilizer use for each option is given in Table 5.3b. The difference in the reduction in net farm income associated with the change in nitrogen fertilizer use is significant between the high-leaching-potential cropland and moderate-leaching-potential cropland. For example, at a nitrogen fertilizer price of $0.20 per pound, the decrease in net farm income when residual nitrogen is reduced by one pound under the soybeans-corn rotation in areas with a moderate potential for leaching is nearly six times as great as that found in areas with a high potential for leaching ($0.17 per pound vs $0.03 per pound). Analogous results hold over the range of nitrogen fertilizer prices considered. It can be concluded that reducing residual nitrogen in soils with a moderate leaching potential results in a greater decline in net farm income than would be realized if the soil has a high potential for leaching.

---

12 If the nitrogen fertilizer price is greater than $0.35, then the fertilizer application rate for corn production on the oats-meadow-corn rotation will be zero.

Table 5.2a. Steady-State Nitrogen Fertilizer Application Rates When Nitrogen Fertilizer Use is Constrained

Crop Rotation	Nitrogen Fertilizer Price $0.10	$0.20	$0.30
	Nitrogen Fertilizer Application Rate		
	------Pounds per acre per year------		
Continuous Planting of Corn with No Fertilizer Use Restriction			
-On Cropland with a High Potential for Leaching	313	246	206
-On Cropland with a Moderate Potential for Leaching	255	220	199
Continuous Planting of Corn with a Restriction on Fertilizer Use			
-On Cropland with a High Potential for Leaching	113	113	113
-On Cropland with a Moderate Potential for Leaching	113	113	113
Soybeans-Corn Rotation with a Restriction on Fertilizer Use			
-On Cropland with a High Potential for Leaching	94	94	94
-On Cropland with a Moderate Potential for Leaching	94	94	94
Oats-Meadow-Corn Rotation with a Restriction on Fertilizer Use			
-On Cropland with a High Potential for Leaching	67	67	53
-On Cropland with a Moderate Potential for Leaching	67	67	67

Table 5.2b. Steady-State Net Farm Income When Nitrogen Fertilizer Use is Constrained

Crop Rotation	Nitrogen Fertilizer Price $0.10	$0.20	$0.30
	Net Farm Income ------Dollars per acre------		
Continuous Planting of Corn with No Fertilizer Use Restriction			
-On Cropland with a High Potential for Leaching	156	134	116
-On Cropland with a Moderate Potential for Leaching	164	145	128
Continuous Planting of Corn with a Restriction on Fertilizer Use			
-On Cropland with a High Potential for Leaching	119	110	101
-On Cropland with a Moderate Potential for Leaching	119	110	101
Soybeans-Corn Rotation with a Restriction on Fertilizer Use			
-On Cropland with a High Potential for Leaching	134	130	127
-On Cropland with a Moderate Potential for Leaching	134	130	127
Oats-Meadow-Corn Rotation with a Restriction on Fertilizer Use			
-On Cropland with a High Potential for Leaching	102	100	97
-On Cropland with a Moderate Potential for Leaching	102	106	97

Table 5.3a. Reduction in Net Farm Income When Switching from Continuous Planting of Corn Without Nitrogen Fertilizer Use Restriction to Crop Rotations With Nitrogen Fertilizer Use Restriction

	Nitrogen Fertilizer Price		
Crop Rotation	$0.10	$0.20	$0.30
	Average Net Farm Income ------Dollars per acre------		
On Cropland with a High Leaching Potential			
Continuous Planting of Corn	37	24	15
Soybeans-Corn Rotation	22	4	-9
Oats-Meadow-Corn Rotation	54	34	19
On Cropland with a Moderate Leaching Potential			
Continuous Planting of Corn	45	35	27
Soybeans-Corn Rotation	30	15	1
Oats-Meadow-Corn Rotation	62	45	31

Note that it is assumed that the prices of corn, soybeans, oats and meadow are $2.35 per bushel, $5.45 per bushel, $1.45 per bushel, and $58 per ton, respectively.

Table 5.3b. Reduction in Average Net Farm Income Per Pound Reduction in Residual Nitrogen Fertilizer Use When Switching from Continuous Planting of Corn Without Nitrogen Fertilizer Use Restriction to Crop Rotations with a Nitrogen Fertilizer Use Restriction

	Nitrogen Fertilizer Price		
Crop Rotation	$0.10	$0.20	$0.30
	---Dollars per one pound of reduction in residual nitrogen---		
On Cropland with a High Leaching Potential			
Continuous Planting of Corn	0.21	0.21	0.19
Soybeans-Corn Rotation	0.13	0.03	-0.12
Oats-Meadow-Corn Rotation	0.35	0.30	0.24
On Cropland with a Moderate Leaching Potential			
Continuous Planting of Corn	0.40	0.40	0.40
Soybeans-Corn Rotation	0.25	0.17	0.02
Oats-Meadow-Corn Rotation	0.52	0.52	0.46

Note that it is assumed that the prices of corn, soybeans, oats and meadow are $2.35 per bushel, $5.45 per bushel, $1.45 per bushel, and $58 per ton, respectively.

CONCLUSIONS

This chapter is concerned with costs to a profit-maximizing farmer to comply with a restriction on nitrogen fertilizer use on cropland vulnerable to nitrate leaching. The compliance cost associated varying levels of cropland vulnerability to nitrate leaching are theoretically and empirically investigated using a farm-level dynamic programming model considering the nitrogen carry-over effect. Theoretical results indicate that it is indeterminate whether cropland with a high leaching potential will have smaller or larger compliance cost than cropland with a moderate leaching potential when nitrogen fertilizer use is constrained. An empirical investigation based on an Iowa case study, however, concludes that a fertilizer use restriction on cropland highly vulnerable to leaching will have a smaller compliance cost (i.e., a lower cost to the farmer) per acre and a smaller compliance cost per pound reduction in nitrogen fertilizer application rate relative to cropland with a moderate leaching potential. The per acre cost difference between these two types of cropland is relatively insignificant. The cost per-pound reduction in residual nitrogen, however, can be quite significant. Policy makers interested in determining an equitable financial incentive to compensate a farmer to reduce nitrogen fertilizer use aimed at mitigating a potential nitrate leaching problem should not base their decision on the vulnerability of cropland to leaching. Rather, the decision must be based on an empirical assessment.

REFERENCES

Aldrich, S. "Nitrogen Management to Minimize Adverse Effects on the Environment," Chapter 47 in *Nitrogen in Crop Production*, Soil Science Society of America, Madison, WI. 1984.

Baumol W., and W. Oates, *The Theory of Environmental Policy*, 2nd edition, Cambridge University Press, Cambridge, 1988.

Beattie, B. and C. Taylor, *The Economics of Production*, John Wiley & Sons, New York, NY, 1985.

Blackmer, A., "Losses and Transport of Nitrogen From Soil," Chapter 5 in *Rural Groundwater Contamination*, Edited by F. D'Itri and L. Wolfson, Lewis Publishers Inc., Chelsea, MI, 1987.

Blackmer, A., D. Potter, M. Cerrato, and J. Webb, "Correlations between Soil Nitrate Concentrations in Late Spring and Corn Yields in Iowa," *Journal of Production Agriculture*, Vol. 33(1988), pp. 23-42.

Cantor, P., "Health Effects of Agrichemicals in Groundwater: What Do We Know?" *Agricultural Chemicals and Groundwater Protection: Emerging Management and Policy*, Proceedings of a Conference held at St. Paul, MN, October 22-23, 1988.

Duffy, M., and D. Judd, "Estimated Costs of Crop Production in Iowa - 1991," FM-1712, Iowa State University Extension, Iowa State University, Ames, IA, 1991.

Economic Research Service, *Agricultural Outlook*, AO-165, U.S. Department of Agriculture, Washington, DC, September 1990.

Economic Research Service, *The 1990 Farm Act and the 1990 Budget Reconciliation Act*, Economic Research Service, U.S. Department of Agriculture, Washington, DC, December 1990.

Freshwater Foundation, *Nitrates and Groundwater: A Public Health Concern*, The Freshwater Foundation's Health and Environment Network, Navarre, MN, 1988.

Fertilizer Institute, *The Fertilizer Handbook*, 2nd edition, The Fertilizer Institute, Washington, DC, 1976.

Frank, M., B. Beattie, and M. Embleton, "A Comparison of Alternative Crop Response Models," *American Journal of Agricultural Economics*, Vol. 72 (1990), pp. 597-603.

Gill, M. and S Daberkow, "Crop Sequences Among 1990 Major Field Crops and Associated Farm Program Participation," in *Agricultural Resources: Inputs Situation and Outlook Report*, AR-24, Economic Research Service U.S. Department of Agriculture, Washington, DC, October 1991.

Heimlich, R., "Green Payments as a Policy Option," in *Agricultural Outlook 219*, Economic Research Service, U.S. Department of Agriculture, Washington, DC, June 1995.

Huang, W. and R. Lantin, "A Comparison of Farmers' Compliance Costs to Reduce Excess Nitrogen Fertilizer Use Under Alternative Policy Options," *Review of Agricultural Economics*, Vol. 15 (1993), pp. 51-62.

Huang, W. and N. Uri, "The Effect of Farming Practices on Reducing Excess Nitrogen Fertilizer Use," *Environment International*, Vol. 19 (1993), pp. 179-191

Iowa State University Experiment Station at Kanawha, *Experiment Station Report ORC87-14,22*, Iowa State University, Ames, IA, 1986.

Kennedy, J., "Rules for Optimal Fertilizer Carryover," *Review of Marketing and Agricultural Economics*. Vol. 54 (1986), pp. 3-10.

Meisinger, J., "Evaluating Plant-Available Nitrogen in Soil-Crop Systems," Chapter 26 in *Nitrogen in Crop Production*, Soil Science Society of America, Madison, WI. 1984.

Nielsen, E. and L. Lee, *The Magnitude and Costs of Groundwater Contamination From Agricultural Chemicals: A National Perspective*, AER-576, Economic Research Service, U.S. Department of Agriculture, Washington, DC, October 1987.

Office of Technology Assessment, *Protecting the Nation's Groundwater From Contamination*, U.S. Government Printing Office, Washington, DC, 1984.

Paris, Q., "The von Liebig Hypothesis," *American Journal of Agricultural Economics*, Vol. 74 (1992), pp. 1017-28.

Schaffer, M., A. Halvorson, and F. Pierce, "Nitrate Leaching and Economic Analysis Package (NELP): Model Description and Application," in R. Follett (ed.), *Managing Nitrogen for Groundwater Quality and Farm Profitability*, Soil Science Society of America, Madison, WI, 1990.

Takayama, A., *Mathematical Economics*, 2nd Edition, Cambridge University Press, Cambridge, 1988.

Taylor, C., "Certainty Equivalence for Determination of Optimal Fertilizer Application Rates with Carry-over," *Western Journal of Agricultural Economics*, Vol. 8 (1983), pp. 85-97.

Taylor, C., and E. Swanson, "Economic Impact of Imposing Per Acre Restrictions on Use of Nitrogen Fertilizer in Illinois," *Illinois Agricultural Economics*, Vol. 52 (1974), pp. 1-5.

U.S. Congress, *Food, Agricultural, Conservation, and Trade Act of 1990*, 101st Congress, 2d Session, Report 101-916, U.S. Government Printing Office, Washington, DC, 1990.

U.S. Environmental Protection Agency, *National Statistical Assessment of Rural Water Conditions*, U.S. Environmental Protection Agency, Washington, DC, June 1984.

U.S. Environmental Protection Agency, *National Survey of Pesticides in Drinking Water Wells*, Phase I Report, EPA 570/9-90-015, U.S. Environmental Protection Agency, Washington, DC, November 1990.

Voss R. and W. Shrader, *Crop Rotations: Effect on Yields and Response to Nitrogen*, Iowa State University Extension, Iowa State University, Ames, IA, February 1988.

Vroomen, H., and H. Taylor, *Fertilizer Use and Price Statistics, 1960-91*, Statistical Bulletin No. 842, Economic Research Service, U.S. Department of Agriculture, Washington, DC, November 1992.

Williams, J., and D. Krissel, "Water Percolation: An Indicator of N Leaching Potential," in R. Follett (ed.), *Managing Nitrogen for Groundwater Quality and Farm Profitability*, Soil Science Society of America, Madison WI, 1990.

Williams, J., P. Dyke, W. Fuchs, V. Benson, O. Rice, and E. Taylor, *EPIC-Erosion/Productivity Impact Calculator: User Manual*, USDA-ARS Technical Bulletin Number 1768, U.S. Department of Agriculture, Temple, TX, 1990.

CHAPTER 5 APPENDIX

Derivation of the Stochastic Rule for Optimal Nitrogen Fertilizer Application Rates

Kennedy's direct dynamic programming method is used to derive the stochastic rule to determine optimal nitrogen fertilizer application rate. The crop yield response in period t is given as $Y_t(n_t,d_t)$ where n_t is available nitrogen and δ_t is a random variable. The portion of nitrogen loss from time period t to t+1 is $K_t(w_t,\varepsilon_t)$ where w_t is a weather and site-specific variable and e_t is a random variable. The fraction of nitrogen carried-over from time period t to time period t+1 is $(1 - K_t(w_t,\varepsilon_t))$.

The problem is to maximize the expected net farm income

(5A.1)

$$\text{Max}_{a_1\cdots a_m} \sum_{t=1}^{m} \alpha^{t1}\ E\,[\,\alpha\, P_t^y\, Y_t(\,n_t,\delta_t\,))\, p_t^f\ a_t\,]$$

subject to

$$n_t = x_t + a_t$$
$$x_{t+1} = (1 - K_t(w_t, \varepsilon_t)(n_t - \nu Y_t(n_t, \delta_t))$$
$$a_t \geq 0$$
$$\text{with } x_1 \text{ given}$$

The recursive functional equation of problem (5A.1) is

5A.2

$$\zeta_t\{x_t\} = \text{Max}_{a_t} E[\alpha\, p_t^y Y_t(n_t, \delta_t) - p_t^f a_t + \alpha \zeta_{t+1}\{x_{t+1}\}] \qquad \text{for } t = m, \ldots, 1$$
$$\text{where}$$
$$n_t = x_t + a_t$$
$$x_{t+1} = (1 - K_t(w_t, \varepsilon_t)(n_t - \nu Y_t(n_t, \delta_t))$$
$$a_t \geq 0$$
$$\zeta_{m+1}\{x_{m+1}\} = 0$$

The dynamic programming problem (5A.2) can be expressed as

5A.3

$$\zeta_t\{x_t\} = \alpha E[\, p_t^y Y_t(x_t + a_t^*, \delta_t) - p_t^f a_t^*\,] + \alpha \zeta_{t+1}\{E[x_{t+1}]\}$$

$$\text{for } t = 1, \ldots, m$$

$$\text{where } a_1^* \ldots a_m^* \text{ are the optimal rates}$$

Assuming concavity of the function (5A.3), that $E[p^y_t]$ is known, and that $a^*_t \geq 0$ for all t, the first order condition is

(5A.4)

$$\alpha E[\,p_t^y\,]\partial E[Y_t(n_t t, \delta_t)]/\partial a_t - p_t^f + \alpha E[(\partial x_{t+1}/\partial a_t)(\partial \zeta_{t+1}/\partial x_{t+1})] = 0$$
$$\text{for } t = 1, \ldots, m$$

Partially differentiating (5A.2) with respect to x_t gives

(5A.5)

$$\partial \zeta_t/\partial x_t = \alpha E[\,p_t^y\,]\partial E[Y_t(n_t, \delta_t)]/\partial a_t + \alpha E[(\partial x_{t+1}/\partial a_t)(\partial \zeta_{t+1}/\partial x_{t+1})]$$
$$\text{for } t = 1, \ldots, m$$

Since the terms on the right hand side of equation (5A.5) equal p^f_t as shown in equation (5A.4), equation (5A.5) becomes

(5A.6) $\partial z_t / \partial x_t = p^f_t$.

Substituting p^f_{t+1} for $\partial z_{t+1} / \partial x_{t+1}$, and $(1\text{-}K_t(w_t,\varepsilon_t))(r_t\text{-}v\ Y_t(n_t,\delta_t))$ for x_{t+1} in equation (5A.4) gives

(5A.7)

$$\alpha E[\, p^y_t \,]\partial E[\, Y_t(n_t,\delta_t)]/\partial a_t = p^f_t - \alpha\, E[(1 - K_t(\, w_t,\varepsilon_t\,))(1 - v\partial\, Y_t(\, n_t,\varepsilon_t\,)/\partial a_t\,)\, p^f_{t+1}] \quad for\ t = 1,...,m$$

It is further assumed that the nitrogen fertilizer price and nitrogen carry-over are independent, the portion of nitrogen leaching and the amount of nitrogen available for leaching are independent, and the fertilizer price is a random variable and is conditional on the price from the previous year. Equation (5A.7) becomes

(5A.8)

$$\alpha E[\, p^y_t\,]\, \partial E[\, Y_t(n_t,\delta_t)]/\partial a_t = p^f_t - \alpha(1 - E[\, K_t(\, w_t,\varepsilon_t\,)])(1 - v\partial E[\, Y_t(\, n_t,\delta_t\,)]/\partial a_t\,)\, E[\, p^f_{t+1} \mid p^f_t\,] \quad for\ t = 1,...,m$$

Chapter 6

MARKET-BASED INCENTIVES FOR ADDRESSING NON-POINT WATER QUALITY PROBLEMS: A RESIDUAL NITROGEN TAX APPROACH

INTRODUCTION

Taxes are only one of a number of policy instruments available to address externalities arising from agricultural production. Alternatives range from moral suasion and command and control approaches to market based incentives including taxes, subsidies, and permit schemes. Policy instruments based on direct market incentives can be shown to be the least cost solution to the problem of attaining ambient environmental standards. Market-based instruments are not only statically superior leading to the least cost solution to pollution abatement, but also provide inducements to technological innovation. Taxes, for example, use market mechanisms to transmit information by charging a price for currently unpriced services provided by the environment. Economists have, therefore, been critical of policy approaches that depend on direct regulation and either ambient or technological standards because they promote inefficiency and inequity. Despite this criticism, regulatory authorities have favored command and control approaches to pollution regulation for non-point sources (Baumol and Oates [1988]).

A number of practical and institutional obstacles have restricted the widespread adoption of market-based pollution control instruments. Baumol and Oates [1988] and Pezzey [1988] offer a number of explanations for the traditionally limited role of taxes. A primary obstacle is that optimal Pigovian taxes require the regulator to know marginal external cost functions and marginal net benefit functions. It is unrealistic, however, to expect that either the marginal cost or benefit functions are known with sufficient accuracy to calculate optimal an optimal tax rate. Instead, the regulator's second-best position must be to develop approximations of the functions to obtain rough estimates of damages and benefits. This kind of information provides "ballpark" indications of the effects of policy intervention.

A second major obstacle is producers' resistance to new taxes because taxes are likely to reduce profits. Commingled with the obvious objection about reduced profitability are concerns about ever-increasing taxes and institutional and social inertia supporting the status quo. Taxes are a relatively new idea for dealing with pollution regulation. A regulatory change in instruments requires advocates of market-based incentives to demonstrate their alternatives are superior to those currently in place and not simply articulate the desirable characteristics of taxes.

An optimal Pigovian tax is based directly on the level of the pollutant in the environment. Because a nitrogen tax, for example, targets the use of the nitrogen fertilizer input and does not directly alter the level of the pollutant, it is an indirect instrument for mitigating non-point water quality problems associated with agricultural production. Defining agricultural nitrogen pollution as non-point implies the presence of high information costs that prohibit the direct taxation of the pollutant. Instead, a second-best approach is to tax the input causing to the water quality problem and, thereby, indirectly mitigate the environmental stress.[1]

The implications of imposing an ad valorem tax to reduce nitrogen pollutants have been examined in a number of studies including those by Diebel et al. [1988], Lambert [1990], Huang and Lantin [1993], Taylor 1975], Palmini et al. [1977], and Hrubovcak et al. [1990]. Each of these studies examine the effects of imposing an ad valorem tax which increases the per unit cost of nitrogen fertilizer. The potential effect of imposing an ad valorem nitrogen tax for reducing non-point pollution is based on profit seeking by farmers who equate the marginal cost of nitrogen to its marginal value in production. Farmers use less nitrogen in crop production if the marginal cost of nitrogen increases, all other things constant. Imposing an ad valorem nitrogen tax raises the cost of nitrogen, reduces nitrogen use, and decreases the nitrogen available for potential leaching into groundwater.

Proposals advancing ad valorem taxes on all nitrogen fertilizer use have been criticized. It is argued that a uniform tax on all farmers penalizes most heavily farmers growing crops with high nitrogen requirements who are not necessarily the greatest polluters. Moreover, a simple ad valorem tax ignores nitrogen absorbed and removed from the field when crops are harvested. Nitrogen removed from the field is unavailable for leaching. A credible policy instrument must provide disincentives to input use for polluters and not all users. Since input use varies by soil type, crop, and farming and management practice, the appropriate tax rate, therefore, must vary by location or region and by crop.

Because a simple ad valorem tax taxes all nitrogen purchased by all farmers, the tax penalizes farmers using nitrogen efficiently, where efficiency is defined as yield obtained for each unit of nitrogen applied. Imposing a tax on efficient farmers does not reduce nitrogen in the soil available for potential leaching. Instead, the tax distorts the optimal mix of production inputs and imposes unnecessary financial burdens on efficient farmers.

---

[1] A nitrogen fertilizer tax has been implemented in Iowa to generate revenue for research and extension activities in water quality improvement. The tax revenue is used to develop and to promote the adoption of alternative farming practices to reduce nitrate leaching.

A RESIDUAL NITROGEN TAX

Applying excess nitrogen on crops and the presence of excess nitrogen already in the soil are the main sources of potential nitrate leaching into groundwater (Meisinger [1984] and Blackmer [1987]). Reducing nitrogen use and removing excess nitrogen from the soil are straightforward approaches to reduce the potential for nitrate leaching. A residual nitrogen tax is an alternative to the simple ad valorem tax aimed at reducing nitrogen fertilizer use and removing excess nitrogen from the soil. A residual nitrogen tax is levied on the nitrogen applied in excess of nitrogen removed and rewards farmers for removing nitrogen from the soil in excess of the amount of nitrogen applied. This tax targets nitrogen polluters not efficient nitrogen fertilizer users.

A residual nitrogen tax is characterized in the following way. First, a farmer pays a simple ad valorem nitrogen tax for all nitrogen purchased. After the crop is harvested and removed from the field, the farmer receives a tax refund for the amount of nitrogen removed from the field. If the farmer has applied more nitrogen than is removed, the farmer pays the tax. If the nitrogen removed is equal to the amount applied, then the tax is zero. If the nitrogen removed exceeds the amount applied, then the farmer receives a subsidy (a negative tax) for reducing soil nitrogen. This is referred to as nitrogen mining.

A simple farm-level model can be used to illustrate the workings of a residual nitrogen tax. Let $y_{ij}(n_{ij})$ be crop j's per-acre yield. It is specified as a function of the nitrogen fertilizer application rate, n_{ij}, on farm i. Let p_j be the price of crop j, k_j is the amount of nitrogen in one unit of harvested crop j, t_{ij} is the residual nitrogen tax rate for each pound of residual nitrogen applied to crop j, and r is the nitrogen fertilizer price. The difference between the nitrogen applied, n_{ij}, and the nitrogen removed $k_jy_{ij}(n_{ij})$ is used to compute the tax liability.

The farmer's objective function is to maximize per acre profits. It is given as

$$(6.1a)\quad z_{ij} = p_jy_{ij}(n_{ij}) - rn_{ij} - t_{ij}[n_{ij} - k_jy_{ij}(n_{ij})] - o_{ij}$$

where z_{ij} is net farm income per acre, t_{ij} is the residual nitrogen tax rate, and o_{ij} is all other per acre production costs. The term $t_{ij}[n_{ij} - k_jy_{ij}(n_{ij})]$ is the residual nitrogen tax. If $n_{ij} > k_jy_{ij}(n_{ij})$, the tax is positive. If $k_jy_{ij}(n_{ij}) > n_{ij}$, soil nitrogen mining occurs and the farmer receives a subsidy. Equation (6.1a) can also be expressed as

$$(6.1b)\quad z_{ij} = p_jy_{ij}(n_{ij}) - (r + t_{ij})n_{ij} + t_{ij}(k_jy_{ij}(n_{ij})) - o_{ij}.$$

In this relationship the farmer pays a simple ad valorem tax, $t_{ij}n_{ij}$, at the time of purchase and receives a refund, $t_{ij}(k_jy_{ij}(n_{ij}))$, for nitrogen removed during harvest. The farmer will remove excess soil nitrogen if the refund from removing the nitrogen is greater than the value of crop loss due to reducing the nitrogen fertilizer application.

ESTIMATING RESIDUAL NITROGEN

The residual nitrogen per acre available for leaching, RN_{ij}, is

$$(6.2)\quad RN_{ij} = n_{ij} + c_{ij} - k_j y_{ij}(n_{ij})$$

where c_{ij} is a nitrogen credit from previous legume crops and other sources such as manure, crop residue, and irrigation water, and $k_j y_{ij}(n_{ij})$ is the amount of nitrogen removed during harvesting crop j.[2] The regulator can determine residual nitrogen because each component of equation (6.2) is estimable.[3] If the amount of nitrogen applied is greater than the amount removed, then excess nitrogen is either stored in the soil (soil-N) or lost through denitrification, runoff, and leaching (Meisinger and Randall [1990]). For vulnerable cropland, excess nitrogen is assumed to be lost through leaching.

Residual nitrogen is estimable from a production (yield) function and a function describing nitrogen removal during harvest. To facilitate exposition, the subscripts i and j are dropped. The function describing nitrogen removed during harvest is assumed to be a linear function of the amount of grain removed.

If a farmer applies nitrogen fertilizer in the amount n_a per acre to maximize net farm income, then residual nitrogen is the difference between n_a, the amount applied and n_z, the amount removed. Residual nitrogen approaches zero as the nitrogen application rate approaches an environmentally optimal nitrogen fertilizer application rate, n_z.

Soil nitrogen is mined when the nitrogen application rate n_a is less than the "environmentally" appropriate application rate n_z. The amount of nitrogen mined is the difference between n_r and n_a. Cropland rich in soil nitrogen is associated with a large intercept term on the production function. As the intercept term for the yield function increases, the amount of nitrogen that can be contributed by the soil for crop production increases. The amount of nitrogen removed from the soil is reduced and approaches zero as the nitrogen application rate approaches n_z.

DETERMINING RESIDUAL NITROGEN TAX RATES

Socially optimal nitrogen use requires that a farmer incur the costs of any environmental damages associated with the use of nitrogen fertilizer. If a more modest objective than optimality is pursued, it is possible to design a residual nitrogen tax that is net social welfare enhancing. A pragmatic approach with respect to non-point water

---

2 Other nitrogen credits should be included under certain circumstances. For example, nitrate level in irrigation water and in precipitation in some areas can be substantial and hence nitrogen credits should be considered.

3 Given the current information and technology available, it is possible to estimate both the amount of nitrogen in harvested crops (grain and plant) and the nitrogen credits from legume crops, manure, crop residue, irrigation water, and precipitation.

quality problems is to design a residual nitrogen tax which treats large regions, for example, a state as a homogenous area in terms of assessing its nitrogen leaching potential. If it is assumed that the objective is to attain a regional sustainable level of soil nitrogen, then four alternative approaches for designing a residual nitrogen tax are available including (a) a crop-farm specific residual nitrogen tax, (b) a farm-specific tax, (c) a regional crop-specific tax, and (d) a uniform regional tax.

(a) A Crop-Farm Specific Residual Nitrogen Tax

With this approach the regulator recognizes differential nitrogen use for each farm and each crop on a farm. Differential use and effects are assumed to be determined by a farm's variability in soil, production practices, and nitrogen uptake by the crops grown. A residual nitrogen tax rate for farm i and crop j is determined by maximizing

(6.3) $z_{ij} = p_j y_{ij}(n_{ij}) - rn_{ij} - o_{ij}$

subject to the constraint

(6.4) $n_{ij} - k_j y_{ij}(n_{ij}) \leq 0.$

That is, the amount of nitrogen applied must be less than or equal to the amount of nitrogen removed from the soil for each crop. The Lagrangean for maximizing equation (6.3) is

(6.5) $L_{ij} = p_j y_{ij}(n_{ij}) - rn_{ij} - o_{ij} + \lambda_{ij}[n_{ij} - k_j y_{ij}(n_{ij})]$

where λ_{ij} is the Lagrangean multiplier, the shadow price of the constraint given by inequality (6.4). If λ_{ij} in equation (6.5) is replaced by t_{ij}, the Lagrangean function (6.5) is identical to the objective function described in equation (6.1a). Maximizing (6.5) is equivalent to maximizing the objective function in (6.1a). Thus, the shadow price obtained from maximizing the Lagrangean function is the optimal residual nitrogen tax rate assuming nitrogen leaching problems differ for each crop and farm. The residual nitrogen tax rate, t_{ij} (shadow price), for crop j and farm i is obtained by solving the first order conditions from equation (6.5). These are

(6.6) $t_{ij}[n_{ij} - k_j y_{ij}(n_{ij})] = 0$

and

(6.7) $(p_j + k_j t_{ij})\,[\partial y_{ij}(n_{ij})/\partial n_{ij}] = t_{ij} + r.$

If it is assumed that $t_{ij} > 0$, the residual nitrogen tax rate, t_{ij}, for crop j and farm i is obtained by solving for the value of n_{ij} from equation (6.6) and then substituting n_{ij} into equation (6.7) to obtain the value for t_{ij}. Both k_j and $y_{ij}(n_{ij})$ are assumed exogenous.

(b) A Farm-Specific Residual Nitrogen Tax

Here the residual nitrogen tax ensures nitrogen applied to all crops on a farm is no greater than the nitrogen removed from harvested crops on that farm. The nitrogen constraint is effective at the farm level and not for specific crops. The regulator determines the appropriate tax by solving

$$(6.8) \qquad t_i \sum_j [n_{ij} - k_j y_{ij}(n_{ij})] = 0$$

and

$$(6.9) \qquad (p_j + k_j t_i)\,[\partial y_{ij}(n_{ij})/\partial n_{ij}] = t_i + r,\ j = 1,2,\ldots,J$$

for t_i ($i = 1,2,\ldots,I$).[4] The relationship represented in equation (6.9) must hold with equality for farmer i to maximize net farm income. The residual nitrogen tax derived under these conditions is applied to all crops on farm i. It is possible for a farmer to use excess nitrogen in the production of one crop while mining soil nitrogen for the production of other crops. Total residual nitrogen generated for farm i is, however, no greater than zero.

(c) A Regional Crop-Specific Tax

The residual nitrogen tax in this case ensures that the amount of nitrogen applied to crop j by all farms in a region is not greater than the amount of nitrogen removed from harvesting that crop in the region. The regulator determines a uniform tax for crop j in the region by solving

$$(6.10) \qquad t_j \sum_i [n_{ij} - k_j\, y_{ij}\,(n_{ij})] = 0$$

and

$$(6.11) \qquad (p_j + k_j\, t_j)\,[\partial y_{ij}(n_{ij})/\partial n_{ij}] = t_j + r,\ i = 1,2,\ldots,I$$

for t_j ($j = 1,2,\ldots,J$).[5] The crop-specific tax is appropriate when there is a dominate crop grown in a region.

(d) A Regional Residual Nitrogen Tax

In this situation the tax must ensure that the aggregate amount of nitrogen applied to all crops by all farms in a given region is no greater than the nitrogen removed from harvested crops. The regulator determines a uniform regional tax rate t for all crops and farms in the region by solving the following first order conditions[6]

---

4 For details on the derivation of a farm-level residual nitrogen tax, see Chapter 6 Appendix A.

5 For details on the derivation of a crop-specific tax rate, see Chapter 6 Appendix B.

6 For details on the derivation of the regional residual nitrogen tax, see Chapter 6 Appendix C.

(6.12) $t \sum_{ij}[n_{ij} - k_j y_{ij}(n_{ij})] = 0$

and

(6.13) $(p_j + k_j t)[\partial y_{ij}(n_{ij})/\partial n_{ij}] = t + r$

for $i = 1,2,...,I$ and $j = 1,2,...,J$

Some farms may mine nitrogen while others may apply excess nitrogen. To produce crop j, farmer i will mine nitrogen if

(6.14) $\partial y_{ij}(n_{ij})/\partial n_{ij})|_{rfn=0} < (t + r)/(p_j + k_j t)$,

and will leave residual nitrogen in the soil if

(6.15) $\partial y_{ij}(n_{ij})/\partial n_{ij})|_{rfn=0} > (t + r)/(p_j + k_j t)$

where rfn = 0 indicates $n_{ij} - k_j y_{ij}(n_{ij}) = 0$ for crop j on farm i. For the region as a whole, residual nitrogen is no greater than zero.

Each of these four types of residual nitrogen taxes - t_{ij}, t_i, t_j, and t - will ensure that residual nitrogen in a region is no greater than zero. Because each type of tax may impose a different tax rate on an individual farmer in a region, their impacts on regional crop production and net farm income can be different. A regional uniform tax is preferable to the others if it results a relatively smaller reduction in regional net farm income.

CASE STUDY - CORN PRODUCTION WITH A TAX

(a) Overview

The objectives of this case study are to illustrate the differential impact on corn farmers in the Corn Belt region of the United States in the presence of a uniform regional residual nitrogen tax and to evaluate its effectiveness in reducing residual nitrogen. Corn is selected for study because it is the largest user of nitrogen fertilizer among crops grown.[7] States included in the analysis are Illinois, Indiana, Iowa, Missouri, and Ohio. Farms in each state are represented by sample points in the 1987 National Resources Inventory (NRI) (Uri [1999]). Each state has thousands of sample points (farms) identified with corn production. Each sample point is assumed to have the same corn production function.

The model as depicted by equations (6.12) and (6.13) is used to compute uniform regional tax rates for three different values of the internal nitrogen, k, required by corn.

7 Corn and soybeans are the two major crops grown in the Corn Belt in terms of number of acres planted, while wheat is a distant third. Soybeans, however, is a legume crop which fixes nitrogen and often requires no application of nitrogen fertilizer.

These three values are 0.9 pounds of nitrogen per bushel of corn (N-lb/bu), 1.08 N-lb/bu, and 1.26 N-lb/bu. The value 0.9 N-lb/bu is the requirement for each bushel of corn recommended by the Fertilizer Institute [1976]. The values 1.08 N-lb/bu and 1.26 N-lb/bu are obtained by increasing 0.9 by 20 and 40 percent, respectively. They are values frequently recommended by extension personnel (Central Platte Natural Resource District [1992]).

The corn yield function for the Corn Belt is

$$(6.16)\quad Y = 65.64 + 0.730N - 0.0017N^2.$$

The function is derived from the Iowa State University research farm study at Kanawha, Iowa (Iowa State University Experiment Station [1986] and Duffy and Chase [1988]). The yield function given in equation (6.16) relates corn yield to nitrogen fertilizer application when corn is planted continuously on the same cropland. This estimate is assumed to be a representative yield function for all farms in the Corn Belt.

This yield function is used to compute uniform regional residual nitrogen tax rates. Given this yield function, and assuming the price of corn is \$2.30 per bushel and the price of nitrogen fertilizer is \$0.15 per pound, the efficient nitrogen fertilizer application rate is 195 pounds per acre. The residual nitrogen tax rates for each k value are determined from equations (6.12) and (6.13).[8] For k = 0.9, 1.08, and 1.26 N-lb/bu, the respective tax rates are \$0.92, \$0.49, and \$0.14 for each pound of nitrogen fertilizer purchased. The respective nitrogen application rates, in the presence of these nitrogen taxes, are 114, 148, and 179 pounds per acre.

The estimate of residual nitrogen in each state is based on the Nutrient Accounting Data Base (NADB) (Huang et al. [1992]). The NADB contains 1987 NRI sample points. Each sample point contains data on acres of crop planted, crop yield and the associated nitrogen application rate, and the crops planted in previous years. There are thousands of sample points in each state and each sample point is treated as a farm. The yield and nitrogen application rate for each sample point in NADB are estimated from the *1990 Cropping Practices Survey* (National Agricultural Statistics Service [1991]). Nitrogen credits from previous legume crops are computed based on data suggested by Meisinger and Randall [1990]. Nitrogen from other sources such as manure is not included in this case study because credible information is just not available. The residual nitrogen to be taxed (or subsidized) for each sample point in each state is computed based on relationship (6.2). The computed residual nitrogen at each sample point (farm) within each state is then summed to obtain the aggregate estimate. The amount of nitrogen

---

8 In this case study, only one crop (corn) is considered. The same yield function (6.16) is assumed for each farm represented by a NRI sample point. The first order conditions (6.12) and (6.13), thus collapse into two equations: $t\,(n_1 - k_1\, y(n_1)) = 0$ and $(p_1 + k_1\, t)[\partial y(n_1)/\partial n_1] = 0$, where subscript 1 refers to corn. Using these two conditions, the tax rate t is computed. Since the yield function is a quadratic function, two roots are obtained when the relationships are solved. The positive root is used.

mined is also estimated. Mining occurs if the computed residual nitrogen associated with a sample point is negative. That is, more nitrogen is removed than applied.

(b) Case Study Results

Results from the case study are presented in two tables. Table 6.1 shows estimated financial results after imposing a residual nitrogen tax. Farmers are assumed to maintain pre-tax nitrogen application rates despite the presence of a nitrogen tax. Table 6.2 shows the effects on residual nitrogen after imposing a nitrogen tax. Farmers are assumed to fully adjust the nitrogen application rate to reduce residual nitrogen to zero in order to avoid the tax or to remove nitrogen from the soil in order to receive a subsidy.

The nitrogen tax has differential impacts on farmers in different Corn Belt states. For example, Illinois farmers incur the largest tax because they have the largest amount of residual nitrogen left on the field. Also, Illinois farmers pay the highest tax per acre. Alternatively, Iowa farmers receive the largest subsidy because they remove the largest amount of nitrogen from the soil. As a result, farmers in Illinois have the largest tax burden and farmers in Iowa have the lowest. For k =1.08, a value frequently used by extension personnel, the tax is \$17.46 per acre in Illinois while in Iowa the tax is \$12.67 per acre (Table 6.1).

Tax revenue collected and subsidies dispensed are sensitive to the assumed k value. When the value of k is less than 1.08, each Corn Belt State generates positive tax revenues. As the value of k increases to 1.26, the subsidies exceed collected tax revenue in every state. For example, in Illinois a total of about \$543 (\$556 - \$13) million in tax revenue is generated when k = 0.9 and \$165 (\$181 - \$16) million if k = 1.08. When k = 1.26, however, net farm income is -\$11.05 (\$0.95 - \$12.0) million. That is, government subsidies for mining soil nitrogen exceed the tax revenue collected.

The total reduction in nitrogen shown in Table 6.2 is the sum of the reduction in the amount of the residual nitrogen plus the amount of nitrogen in the soil removed. The tax has varying impacts on reducing soil nitrogen. For example, for k=1.08, about 405 (34 + 371) million pounds of nitrogen is reduced in Illinois, while about 79 (1.7 + 77.9) million pounds of nitrogen is reduced in Missouri.

The effectiveness of the government subsidy to reduce soil nitrogen differs among states. For example, for k=1.08, each subsidy dollar spent in Illinois yields approximately a 24 (405) 16.7) pound reduction in nitrogen, while in Ohio, about 106 (163) 1.54) pounds of nitrogen is reduced for each dollar spent. This is the largest nitrogen reduction per dollar subsidy among the Corn Belt States. Iowa generates only 6.8 pounds of nitrogen reduction for each dollar spent, the lowest of any of the Corn Belt States.

The impact of the tax on corn production also varies among the states. The percentage reduction in production is the smallest in Iowa and the largest in Illinois for values of k between 0.9 and 1.26 (Table 6.2).[9]

9 The production reduction is estimated as follow. Recall that each sample point has a corn yield value, y, and an associated nitrogen fertilizer application rate value, n. First, substitute n in the yield function (6.16) to obtain yield y_1. Second, use y to estimate the amount of nitrogen removed n_1 using the relationship $n_1 = k\ y$. Next, substitute n in the yield function

Table 6.1. Estimated Financial Impacts of Imposing a Residual Nitrogen Tax (Application Rates Constant)

	Illinois	**Indiana**	**Iowa**	**Missouri**	**Ohio**
Acres Planted (millions)	11.3	6.8	11.9	2.7	5.4
		k = 0.9 pounds/bushel			
Acres Mined (thousands)	756	90	1,720	0	96
N Removed (thousand pounds)	14,645	1,933	20,798	0	1,216
N Left (thousand pounds)	605,167	324,349	419,037	130,910	281,815
Net N Left (thousand pounds)	590,522	322,416	398,239	130,910	280,599
Subsidy (thousand dollars)	13,477	1,778	19,134	0	1,119
Tax Revenue (thousand dollars)	556,753	298,401	385,514	120,437	259,270
Subsidy/acre (dollars/acre)	17.83	19.76	11.12	0	11.65
Tax/acre (dollar/acre)	52.80	44.47	37.87	44.60	48.88
		k = 1.08 pounds/bushel			
Acres Mined (thousand)	893	349	4,150	374	115
N Removed (thousand pounds)	34,159	9,287	85,750	1,701	3,144
N Left (thousand pounds)	370,919	180,116	200,435	77,956	160,146
Net N Left (thousand pounds)	336,760	170,829	114,695	76,255	157,005
Subsidy (thousand dollars)	16,737	4,551	42,018	833	1,540
Tax Revenue (thousand dollars)	181,750	88,257	98,212	38,197	78,470
Subsidy/acre (dollars/acre)	18.74	13.04	10.12	2.22	13.39
Tax/acre (dollars/acre)	17.46	13.68	12.67	16.42	14.84

(6.16) to obtain a yield estimate y_2. Fourth, compute the difference between y_1 and y_2. It is the reduction in corn yield for that sample point. This process is repeated for all sample points. Finally, sum up the yield differences for all sample points in a state to obtain the reduction in production for that state.

Table 6.1. Estimated Financial Impacts of Imposing a Residual Nitrogen Tax (continued)

k = 1.26 pounds/bushel					
Acres Mined (thousand)	4,450	2,876	8,204	818	2,242
N Removed (thousand pounds)	88,316	55,317	233,891	14,266	36,847
N Left (thousand pounds)	6,812	3,876	3,703	1,908	3,169
Net N Left (thousand pounds)	-81,504*	-51,441	-230,188	-12,358	-33,678
Subsidy (thousand dollars)	-12,364	-7,744	-32,744	-1,997	-5,158
Tax Revenue (thousand dollars)	953	542	518	267	443
Subsidy/acre (dollars/acre)	2.78	2.69	3.99	2.44	2.30
Tax/acre (dollars/acre)	0.14	0.14	0.14	0.14	0.14

Note that a negative sign means that more nitrogen is removed than nitrogen left on the field.

Table 6.2. Estimated Residual Nitrogen in the Presence of Taxes (Application Rates Variable)

	Illinois	Indiana	Iowa	Missouri	Ohio
Acres Planted (millions)	11.3	6.8	11.9	2.7	5.4
k = 0.9 pounds/bushel					
N Removed (thousand pounds)	14,645	1,933	20,798	0	1,216
N Reduced (thousand pounds)	605,167	324,348	419,037	130,910	281,815
Total N Reduced (thousand pounds)	619,812	326,281	439,835	130,910	283,031
Subsidy (thousand dollars)	13,473	1,778	19,134	0	1,119
N Removed Per Dollar (lb/dollar)	0.92	0.92	0.92	n*	0.92
N Reduced Per Dollar (lb/dollar)	46.00	183.51	22.98	n	252.93
Production Reduced (percent)	9	8	6	8	9

Table 6.2. Estimated Residual Nitrogen in the Presence of Taxes (continued)

k = 1.08 pounds/bushel					
N Removed (thousand pounds)	34,159	9,287	85,750	1,701	3,144
N Reduced (thousand pounds)	370,919	180,116	200,435	77,956	160,146
Total N Reduced (thousand pounds)	405,078	189,403	286,185	79,657	163,290
Subsidy (thousand dollars)	16,738	4,551	42,018	833	1,540
N Removed Per Dollar (lb/dollar)	2	2	2	2	2
N Reduced Per Dollar (lb/dollar)	24.2	41.6	6.8	95.6	106.0
Production Reduction (percent)	3	3	2	3	3
k = 1.26 pounds/bushel					
N Removed (thousand pounds)	88,316	55,317	233,891	14,266	36,847
N Reduced (thousand pounds)	6,812	3,876	3,703	1,908	3,169
Total N Reduced (thousand pounds)	95,128	59,193	237,594	16,174	40,016
Subsidy (thousand dollars)	12,364	7,744	32,744	1,997	5,158
N Removed Per Dollar (lb/dollar)	7.1	7.1	7.1	7.1	7.1
N Reduced Per Dollar (lb/dollar)	7.6	7.6	7.3	8.1	7.8
Production Reduction (percent)	0.7	0.6	0.2	0.6	0.5

- No nitrogen is removed.

Based on these results, it is apparent that this tax is sensitive to the value of k. In addition impacts on farmers vary significantly among Corn Belt States. An accurate value for k is required to determine an appropriate tax rate. Alternative values for k across states may be used to reflect the variation in production practices and the vulnerability of cropland in each state to nitrogen leaching. Also, it is apparent that the residual nitrogen tax approach can be a cost-effective way for the government to reduce nitrogen available for potential leaching. Each dollar spent reduces nitrogen not only by encouraging farmers to mine excess nitrogen in the soil, but also by discouraging excess nitrogen fertilizer application.

CRITIQUE

The case study for corn illustrates that a residual nitrogen tax can be an important environmental policy tool. Because the residual nitrogen tax eschews command and control regulation, it promotes cost efficient adjustments by farmers while minimizing information costs. This approach allows farmers the freedom to decide which best management practice to adopt to reduce residual nitrogen. Lower information costs for producers and administrators mean lower overall social transaction costs for any equivalent reduction in residual nitrogen and potential nitrogen leaching. Because the residual tax utilizes market-based incentives, it provides farmers, especially those farming on soil susceptible to leaching, monetary signals to seek alternative farming practices that improve the efficiency of nitrogen fertilizer use and reduce nitrogen losses. In addition farmers are encouraged to reduce plantings of crops with high nitrogen requirements while capturing nitrogen carryover in the soil. Moreover, the residual nitrogen tax transforms the current non-point source nitrate pollution problem into a point source problem by making farmers (as the point source) accountable for reducing nitrogen use on each farm and therefore adjusting nitrogen fertilizer use according to site-specific conditions. Finally, a residual nitrogen tax imposes a smaller burden on farmers than an equivalent ad valorem tax (Chapter 6 Appendix D).

The regulatory authority must weigh the regional net social welfare impacts of a proposed residual nitrogen tax, where regional net social welfare is defined as the sum of farm-level net farm income less social damages resulting from production externalities (Weinberg, Kling and Wilen [1993] and Weinberg and Kling [1993]). Furthermore, calculations of net social welfare must include transactions costs associated with implementing a tax. These transaction costs include information, monitoring, enforcement, and administrative costs for the subsidy. These transaction costs can be substantial. Successful implementation of a residual nitrogen tax will require an efficient way to minimize these costs.

Because farmers receive a tax refund on the basis of the estimated nitrogen removed, it is important to accurately estimate yield and k_j to determine the amount of nitrogen removed from the field. Yield can be estimated using historical average yield information. The k_j value can vary from one field to another and from one crop variety to another. It is a function of the harvested yield. Meisinger and Randall [1990] provide an exhaustive survey of the estimates of the common values and the general range of k_j for selected crops in the United States. The estimates reported can provide the basis for determining an appropriate value for k_j. Also, a value for k_j can be determined by laboratory analysis of sampled crops from each field. The cost for an entire region to estimate k_j is, however, prohibitive. A more pragmatic approach is to estimate an average value of k_j for each crop in each homogenous producing region. A feasible alternative is to use the value commonly recommended by agricultural extension agents.

The tax rate, when viewed as the shadow price of the nitrogen constraint, requires knowledge of crop production functions for each farm. Estimating production functions on such a scale is unrealistic. Production functions vary by farm and region because soil type, crop, and production practices differ. One possibility is to first estimate crop production functions for representative farms and use these to determine a uniform tax rate for all crops. Rates can be adjusted as farmers' responses to taxes are observed. Moreover, rates may vary between regions as a function of a region's observed water quality problem.

Other practical problems associated with implementing a nitrogen tax rate involve the level of the tax burden on an individual farmer and the source of financial resources to administer the program. In the case of burden, it is possible for the residual nitrogen tax to make farming unprofitable. If the intent of the regulator is to modify behavior while allowing farming to continue, then some awareness must be given to the absolute level of the tax. Regarding financial resources, while the residual tax program can be configured to be self-financing, it is possible subsidies for nitrogen mining to exceed tax revenue collected.

Conclusions

This chapter outlines a policy aimed at enhancing water quality in general and reducing nitrate leaching into groundwater in particular. Use of a residual nitrogen tax is an approach to induce farmers to limit nitrogen use. It is a cost-effective way to reduce nitrogen available for potential leaching into ground water. This policy option forces farmers to implement a nutrient management plan for efficient nitrogen use. This policy tool can be employed to promote sustainable agricultural production systems to utilize nitrogen from legume crops, animal wastes, and crop residues. Since a tax would likely vary by region, a pilot regional study would be needed to assess the effect of a tax on nitrogen use in selected counties and to address problems associated with implementing the tax including predicting farmers' responses to a tax.

References

Baumol, W. and W. Otes, *The Theory of Environmental Policy*, 2nd edition, Cambridge University Press, Cambridge, 1988.

Blackmer, A., "Losses and Transport of Nitrogen from Soil," Chapter 5 in *Rural Groundwater Contamination*, Edited by Frank M.D'Itri and Lois G. Wolfson, Lewis Publishers Inc., Chelsea, MI, 1987.

Cantor, P., "Health Effects of Agrichemicals in Groundwater: What Do We Know?" *Agricultural Chemicals and Groundwater Protection: Emerging Management and Policy*, Proceedings of a Conference held at St. Paul, MN, October 22-23, 1988.

Central Platte Natural Resources District, *Central Platte NRD's Groundwater Quality Management Program*, Grand Island, NE, January, 1992.

Diebel, P., J. Halstead, R. Kramer, S. Batie, and C. Heatwole, *Managing Agricultural Nitrate Contamination of Groundwater in Rockingham County, Virginia*, SP 88-14

Department of Agricultural Economics, Virginia Polytechnic Institute and State University, Blacksburg, VA, June 1988.

Duffy, M. and C. Chase, "Impacts of 1985 Food Security Act on Crop Rotations and Fertilizer Use," Unpublished manuscript, Department of Agricultural Economics, Iowa State University, Ames, IA, 1988.

Environmental Protection Agency, *National Survey of Pesticides in Drinking Water Wells: Phase I Report*, EPA 570/9-90-015, U.S. Environmental Protection Agency, Washington, DC, November 1991.

Environmental Protection Agency, *Another Look: National Survey of Pesticides in Drinking Water Wells--Phase II Report*, EPA 579/09-91-020, U.S. Environmental Protection Agency, Washington, DC, January 1992.

Fertilizer Institute, *The Fertilizer Handbook*, 2nd edition, The Fertilizer Institute, Washington, DC, 1976.

Hrubovcak, J., M. LeBlanc, and J. Miranowski, "Limitations in Evaluating Environmental Policy Coordination Benefits," *American Economic Reviews*, Vol. 2 (1990), pp. 208-12.

Huang, W. and R. Lantin, "A Comparison of Farmers' Compliance Costs to Reduce Excess Use Under Alternative Policy Options," *Review of Agricultural Economics*, Vol. 15 (1993), pp. 51-62.

Huang, W., D. Westenbarger, and K. Mizer, "The Magnitude and Distribution of U.S. Cropland Vulnerable to Nitrate Leaching," *Making Information Work*, National Governors' Association Conference Proceedings, Washington, DC, January 18-23.

Iowa State University Experiment Station, Kanawha, *Experiment Station Report ORC87-14,22*, Iowa State University, Ames, IA, 1986.

Lambert, D., "Risk Considerations in the Reduction of Nitrogen Fertilizer Use in Agricultural Production," *Western Journal of Agricultural Economics*, Vol. 15 (1990), pp. 234-244.

Lijinksy, W. and S. Epstein, "Nitrosoamine As Environmental Carcinogens," *Nature*, Vol. 225 (1970), pp. 21-23.

Meisinger, J., "Evaluating Plant-Available Nitrogen in Soil-Crop Systems," Chapter 26 in *Nitrogen in Crop Production*, Soil Science Society of America, Madison, WI. 1984.

Meisinger, J. and G. Randall, "Estimating Nitrogen Budgets for Soil-Crop Systems," Chapter 5 in *Managing Nitrogen for Groundwater Quality and Farm Profitability*, Soil Science Society of America, Madison, WI. 1990.

National Agricultural Statistics Service, *1990 Cropping Practices Survey*, United States Department of Agriculture, Washington, DC, 1991.

Palmini, D., C. Taylor, and E. Swanson, *The Potential Economic Impact of Selected Agricultural Pollution Control on Two Counties in Illinois: A Linear Programming Interindustry Approach*, Agricultural Economic Report No. 154, Department of Agricultural Economics, University of Illinois, Urbana, IL, 1977.

Pezzey, J., "Market Mechanisms of Pollution Control: Polluter Pays," in *Sustainable Environment Management: Principles and Practices*, edited by R. Tuaner, Bellhaven Press, Boulder, CO, 1988.

Taylor, C., "A Regional Market for Rights to Use Fertilizer As a Means of Achieving Water Quality Standards," *Journal of Environmental Economics and Management*, Vol. 2 (1975), pp. 7-17.

Uri, N., *Agriculture and the Environment*, NOVA Science Publishers, Commack, NY, 1999.

Weinberg, M., and C. Kling, "The Costs of Piecemeal Agricultural and Environmental Policy Making," a paper presented at the 1993 AAEA Meeting in Orlando, FL, August 1- 4, 1993.

Weinberg, M., C. Kling, and J. Wilen, "Water Markets and Water Quality," *American Journal of Agricultural Economics*, Vol. 75 (1993), pp. 278-91.

CHAPTER 6 APPENDIX A

A Farm-Specific Residual Nitrogen Tax

Assume farm i maximizes net farm income. The net farm income function, z_i, is expressed as

(6A.1) $z_i = \sum_j[p_j\, y_{ij}(n_{ij}) - rn_{ij} - o_{ij}]$

subject to a constraint to ensure that the sum of residual nitrogen from farm i is less than zero given as

(6A.2) $\sum_j[n_{ij} - k_j\, y_{ij}(n_{ij})] \leq 0.$

The Lagrangean for this problem is

(6A.3) $L_i = \sum_j[p_j\, y_{ij}(n_{ij}) - rn_{ij} - o_{ij}] + t_i \sum_j[n_{ij} - k_j y_{ij}(n_{ij})]$

where t_i is the shadow price of the constraint and the residual nitrogen tax rate for forming. Maximizing (6A.3) with respect to n_{ij} and t_i. yields the first order conditions (equations (6.8) and (6.9)).

CHAPTER 6 APPENDIX B

A Regional Crop-Specific Residual Nitrogen Tax

The objective function to be maximized is regional net farm income from the production of crop j. Regional net farm income, z_j, is given as

(6B.1) $z_j = \sum_i[p_j\, y_{ij}(n_{ij}) - rn_{ij} - o_{ij}]$

subject to a constraint to ensure that the regional residual nitrogen from production of crop j is less than zero. This is expressed as

(6B.2) $\sum_i[n_{ij} - k_j\, y_{ij}(n_{ij})] \leq 0.$

The Lagrangean for this problem is

(6B.3) $L_j = \sum_i[p_j\, y_{ij}(n_{ij}) - rn_{ij} - o_{ij}] + t_j \sum_i[n_{ij} - k_j y_{ij}(n_{ij})]$

where t_j is the shadow price of constraint (6B.2) and is the residual nitrogen tax rate for crop j. Maximizing (6B.3) with respect to n_{ij} and t_j yields the first order conditions (equations (6.10) and (6.11)).

CHAPTER 6 APPENDIX C

A Regional Uniform Residual Nitrogen Tax

The objective function maximized is regional net farm income. It is expressed as the sum of net farm income from crops produced in the region. Regional net farm income, z, is

(6C.1) $z = \sum_{ij}[p_j y_{ij}(n_{ij}) - rn_{ij} - o_{ij}]$

subject to a constraint to ensure that total regional residual nitrogen is no greater than zero. This is just

(6C.2) $\sum_{ij}[n_{ij} - k_j y_{ij}(n_{ij})] \leq 0.$

The Lagrangean for this problem is

(6C.3) $L = \sum_{ij}[p_j y_{ij}(n_{ij}) - rn_{ij} - o_{ij}] + t \sum_{ij}[n_{ij} - k_j\, y_{ij}(n_{ij})]$

where t is the shadow price of the constraint (6C.2). It is the uniform regional residual nitrogen tax rate. Maximizing (6C.3) with respect to n_{ij} and t yields the first order conditions (equations (6.12) and (6.13)). By solving these first order conditions, a regional uniform residual tax rate, t, can be determined.

For a regional uniform tax, it can be shown that the Lagrangean (6C.3), which is the aggregate regional net farm income, can be obtained by summing the net farm income of individual farms. Substituting t for t_{ij} in equation (6.1a), the net farm income for crop j of farm i is

(6C.4) $z_{ij} = p_j y_{ij}(n_{ij}) - rn_{ij} - t\,[n_{ij} - k_j y_{ij}(n_{ij})] - o_{ij}$

Summing (6C.4) over i and j yield a value of net farm income of individual farms that is the same as the Lagrangean (6C.3). The solution of the Lagrangean (6C.3), thus, is the same as the solution of (6C.4) for all individual farms in the region.

CHAPTER 6 APPENDIX D

Comparing a Residual Nitrogen Tax with a Simple Ad Valorem Tax

It is demonstrated that a farmer pays less tax with a residual nitrogen tax than with an ad valorem tax which taxes all users at the same rate. This result holds although the residual nitrogen tax rate is higher than the ad valorem tax rate. First, it is demonstrated that the residual nitrogen tax rate is higher than the ad valorem rate.

Denoting t_{ij}^1 as the residual nitrogen tax rate, equation (6.7) can be expressed as

(6D.1) $\partial y_{ij}(n_{ij})/\partial n_{ij} = (t_{ij}^1 + r)/(p_j + k_j\, t_{ij}^1)$.

Denoting t_{ij}^2 as the efficient ad valorem tax rate, one can obtain

(6D.2) $\partial y_{ij}(n_{ij})/\partial n_{ij} = (t_{ij}^2 + r)/p$.

Because the marginal value product at $rfn_{ij}=0$ is the same under either tax,

(6D.3) $(t_{ij}^1 + r)/(p_j + k_j\, t_{ij}^1) = (t_{ij}^2 + r)/p_j$.

Rearranging the terms in equation (6D.3) yields

(6D.4) $(t_{ij}^1 + r)/\,(t_{ij}^2 + r) = (p_j + k_j\, t_{ij}^1)/p_j > 1$

since k_j and t_{ij}^1 are positive values. From relation (6D.4), $(t_{ij}^1 + r) > (t_{ij}^2 + r)$. This implies

(6D.5) $t_{ij}^1 > t_{ij}^2$.

That is, the residual nitrogen tax rate is greater than the simple ad valorem tax rate.

Next, it is shown that a farmer pays less tax under the residual nitrogen tax scenario than under an ad valorem regime. Assume a farmer applies n_a nitrogen before a tax is imposed. In addition n_0 is the nitrogen applied in excess of n_z before taxes. When taxes are imposed

(6D.6) $(n_z + n_0)\, t_{ij}^2 - n_0 t_{ij}^1 > 0$.

If $n_{ij} - k_j\, y_{ij}(n_{ij}) = 0$ holds under both taxes, then n_0 is zero under both tax regimes. Inequality (6D.6) therefore implies

(6D.7) $n_z \, t_{ij}^{\,1} > 0$.

If the farmer is efficient and it is socially desirable to reduce nitrogen use from the current level, n_a, to any arbitrary level n_0, to reduce nitrogen available for potential leaching, then the farmer suffers income loss only from reducing production under the residual nitrogen tax. Under the ad valorem tax, the farmer suffers two sources of income loss - income loss from reducing production which is equal to the reduction under the residual nitrogen tax and the income loss from paying the tax on nitrogen purchased.

Chapter 7

AN EVALUATION OF SOIL NITROGEN TESTING CONSIDERING THE CARRY-OVER EFFECT

INTRODUCTION

Soil nitrogen testing (N-testing) has been promoted as an important method to help in reducing nonpoint-source pollution (Environmental Protection Agency [1993]). It provides information to assist farmers in improving the application and timing of nitrogen fertilizer. It reveals the level of nitrogen in the soil profile enabling a farmer to determine whether and how much additional nitrogen fertilizer is needed for crops, to avoid excess use of nitrogen fertilizer, and consequently to reduce nitrogen fertilizer costs (private costs) as well as nitrogen losses through leaching and runoff (social costs).

There are two types of soil N-testing - pre-plant nitrogen tests (PPNT) and pre-side-dress nitrogen tests (PSNT). PPNT is conducted before planting while PSNT is conducted after planting and before side-dressing nitrogen fertilizer is applied. Because it is the most common and extensively used, just the use of PSNT will be considered here.

The effectiveness of soil N-testing in predicting nitrogen fertilizer needs varies by region because of differences in site-specific characteristics such as precipitation, evapotranspiration, soil type and texture, depth of the root zone and nitrogen carry-over from previous years. Generally, soil N-testing is reported to be effective in the Upper Midwest, the Northeast, and Wisconsin. It is also most effective when applied on fields following a dry year and on those fields with manure applications in the previous year (Bock et al. [1992]).

Interest in soil N-testing has grown in recent years beyond its traditional role in improving farming profitability to include its potential role in reducing offsite water pollution. It has been shown that, in certain situations, soil N-testing can help a farmer enhance net farm income while reducing nitrogen fertilizer use. For example, Shortle et al. [1993] show that soil N-testing may reduce nitrogen fertilizer use and decrease excess nitrogen available for potential leaching and runoff. They also demonstrate, however, the opposite effects are conceptually possible and conclude that the potential economic and environmental gains from the adoption of soil N-testing are empirical issues. Using results from a Pennsylvania farm survey, they find positive economic and environmental benefits associated with the use of soil N-testing. Babcock [1992] shows that temporal uncertainty regarding nitrogen available at the time of fertilizer application can affect the optimal nitrogen fertilizer application rate. Babcock and Blackmer [1992] conclude that use of soil N-testing to remove the temporal uncertainty of nitrate concentration in the soil can reduce average nitrogen fertilizer application rates by up to 38% and can increase net farm income by up to $54 per hectare per year in Iowa. Bosch et al. [1994] find that the effects of soil N-testing on nitrogen fertilizer use are influenced by farmers' attitudes toward risk and by the assumptions regarding the nature of the production function. They show that use of soil N-testing is likely to help risk-averse farmers reduce nitrogen fertilizer use. Analyzing survey data from Nebraska, Fuglie and Bosch [1995] conclude that the economic and environmental benefits of soil N-testing to farmers depends on the cropping history of the cropland (e.g., what crop was grown in prior years), soil characteristics, and whether manure is applied coincident with the nitrogen fertilizer.

While these and other previous economic analyses have been useful in understanding the soil N-testing decision, they have failed to consider the nitrogen carry-over effect. They uniformly assume that in the absence of soil N-testing, nitrogen fertilizer in excess of crop needs is lost from the cropland. Such an assumption may inflate the benefit of soil N-testing by suggesting that nitrogen fertilizer application should be lower than might otherwise be the case. For example, in areas where the nitrate leaching problem is not severe, not all residual (unused) nitrogen will be lost. Instead, some of it will carry-over to the next crop year and can become an important source of nitrogen for the crops. Consequently, in this instance the amount of nitrogen fertilizer that should be optimally applied will be less than if all of the residual nitrogen had been lost.

Given these considerations, the objective of this study is to evaluate the economic and environmental benefits of soil N-testing when information about nitrogen in the soil and available for plant uptake is explicitly considered. The net economic (private) benefit of soil N-testing is the gain in net farm income associated with using soil N-testing to determine the requisite (optimal) application rate of nitrogen fertilizer. The net environmental (social) benefit of soil N-testing is the reduction in nitrogen loss to the environment as a consequence of the use of soil N-testing to reduce the nitrogen fertilizer application rate below what it would be in the absence of such a test. The realization of such benefits are influenced not only by site-specific variables but also by the farmer's current knowledge about best nutrient management practices. In the absence of soil N-testing, a farmer will employ a variety of alternative nitrogen management practices. For example, a farmer may systematically apply nitrogen fertilizer at a rate based on some assumed rate of nitrogen carry-over. This assumed rate can be incorrect. A farmer may use a maximum expected yield goal based on past observations to determine the nitrogen fertilizer application rate. A farmer may use past yield information to update the yield goal when determining the nitrogen fertilizer application rate. The economic and environmental benefits of soil N-testing can be estimated as a farmer switches from one of these practices to the practice of using the pre-side-dress nitrogen test (PSNT). Such an assessment will be carried out in what follows. Data from crops grown at the USDAs

Agricultural Research Service Sustainable Agriculture Demonstration Farm in Southern Maryland will be used in the assessment.

Since the economic and environmental benefits of soil N-testing are site-specific, the results from a field on which soil N-testing is used must be compared with the results from the same field on which no soil N-testing is employed. The comparison will require the use of an economic model and a crop production process model. The economic model, which is developed in the next section, is a dynamic optimization model which determines the optimal nitrogen fertilizer application rate by including the nitrogen carry-over effect. The optimal nitrogen fertilizer application rate is used to provide a benchmark for the soil N-testing evaluation. The crop production process model is a stochastic crop growth model which simulates crop production as a function of carry-over nitrogen and weather variables such as daily precipitation and temperature. The crop production process model is used for two purposes: (1) to generate data for the estimation of a yield function and a carry-over function that are required for the empirical estimation of the optimal nitrogen fertilizer application rate, and (2) to simulate crop production under alternative nitrogen fertilizer management practices when carry-over nitrogen is present.

THE DYNAMIC ECONOMIC OPTIMIZATION MODEL

The economic consequences of adopting soil N-testing is measured by the magnitude of the present value of expected net farm income over a fixed time horizon. The model assumes that farmers maximize net farm income associated with nitrogen fertilizer use. The model provides a dynamic rule which then is used to determine a steady-state nitrogen fertilizer application rate and nitrogen loss to the environment. The steady-state solution of the model is used as the reference point (benchmark) for evaluating the consequences of the adoption of soil N-testing.

Taylor [1983] and Kennedy [1986] (TK) formulate a stochastic dynamic economic model considering the nitrogen carry-over effect. They assume that (1) there exists a stochastic yield function, $y_t = y_t(r_t,\delta_t)$, which is based on available nitrogen r_t and a random variable δ_t, (2) there exists a stochastic carry-over function $h_t = h_t(r_t,\mu_t)$, which is also based on available nitrogen r_t and a random variable μ_t, (3) there is independence between the fertilizer price and the nitrogen carry-over, and (4) there is agronomic equivalence between carry-over nitrogen and applied nitrogen. The TK stochastic dynamic model is formulated to solve the following problem:

Maximize the present value of expected net farm income

(7.1)

$$\text{Max}_{a_1 \ldots a_n} \sum_{t=1}^{n} \alpha^{t-1} E(P_t^y y_t p_t^f a_t)$$

subject to
(7.2)

$$r_t = x_t + a_t$$
$$x_{t+1} = h_t$$
$$a_t \geq 0$$
$$\text{with } x_1 \text{ given}$$

where

a_t is the application rate of nitrogen fertilizer in period t,
p^y_t is the price of the crop,
y_t is a stochastic yield function,
p^f_t is the price of nitrogen fertilizer in period t,
α is the time preference discount factor which is determined by $1/(1+\beta)$, where β is the interest rate
x_t is the amount of nitrogen carried-over to period t,
h_t is the stochastic nitrogen carry-over function, and
r_t is nitrogen available for plant uptake in period t.

Fixed costs are ignored because they do not affect the determination of the amount of nitrogen fertilizer to be applied. The TK stochastic dynamic economic model is clearly designed for a risk-neutral farmer who wants to determine the optimal nitrogen fertilizer application rate in order to maximize the present value of expected net farm income from producing a crop on a field. The fertilizer use decision is assumed to be independent of other input use decisions.

The problem described in equations (7.1) and (7.2) has been solved by TK. Assuming that the expected price of fertilizer in period t+1 can be determined by the fertilizer price in period t, denoted as $E[p^f_{t+1} | p^f_t]$, and that the fertilizer price and the nitrogen carry-over are independent, they derive a deterministic rule for the optimal nitrogen fertilizer application rate. The TK rule is expressed as

$$E[\,p^y_t\,]\,\partial E[\,y_t\,]/\partial a_t = p^f_t - \alpha\,\partial E[\,h_t\,]/\partial a_t\,E[\,p^f_{t+1} | p^f_t\,] \tag{7.3}$$

This rule equates the expected value of the marginal product of nitrogen fertilizer in period t to the nitrogen fertilizer price in period t less the discounted marginal value of nitrogen applied in the current period t to be carried over to the next period t+1. Thus, the solution can be obtained by solving a simple deterministic static certainty equivalence problem (Taylor [1983]).

One potential problem arises from the application of the TK rule. Improper specification of the carry-over function, $h_t(r_t,\mu_t)$, in equation (7.3) can lead to infeasible results.[1]

A proper specification of the nitrogen carry-over function must use a nitrogen mass balance framework. In such a setting, a nitrogen carry-over function can be specified as (7.4)

$$h_t = v_t(r_t - k\, y_t)$$

where $(r_t - k\, y_t)$ is the amount of residual nitrogen available for plant uptake. That is, it is the difference between the total amount of nitrogen available for plant uptake, r_t, and nitrogen in the harvested crop removed from the field, $k\, y_t$, where k is the amount of nitrogen in one unit of the harvested crop. The percentage of residual nitrogen to be carried over to the next period is given by the function, $v_t = v_t(r_t,\varepsilon_t)$. This is a stochastic function of r_t and a random variable e_t. With this carry-over function and given an initial value for x_t, and with the assumption that v_t and the amount of residual nitrogen are independent,[2] the optimal fertilizer application rule becomes[3]
(7.5)

$$\alpha E[\, p_t^y\,]\, \partial E[\, y_t\,]/\partial\, a_t =$$
$$p_t^f - \alpha\partial(E[\, v_t\,]\,(\, r_t - kE[\, y_t\,]))/\partial\, a_t\, E[\, p_{t+1}^f \mid p_t^f\,]$$
$$for\; t = 1,\dots,n$$

---

1 Kennedy [1986] has pointed out that a major shortcoming of specifying the carry-over relationship solely as a function of rt is the absence of any consideration of the significant effect of a harvested crop on the amount of nitrogen carried to next time period. A low crop yield in period t because of low rainfall, for example, can lead to low nitrogen uptake. This leaves more nitrogen than usual to be carried-over to the next period, t+1. On the other hand, a high yield in period t because of favorable weather conditions can lead to high nitrogen uptake leaving less nitrogen than usual to be carried-over to next period, t+1. Specification of a carryover function without explicit consideration of the effect of nitrogen in the harvested crop can violate the nitrogen mass balance relationship and result an infeasible solution. This problem can be corrected when specifying the nitrogen carry-over function by using the nitrogen mass balance principle which includes these effects (Meisinger et al. [1992]).

2 The percentage of residual nitrogen carried to the next time period need not be a simple function of the level of residual nitrogen currently in the soil. It may more realistically be determined by soil characteristics and effective precipitation (Schaffer et al. [1990] and Williams and Krissel [1990]). Therefore, the expected carry-over rate is more properly a function of the average of the annual carry-over rates over time. The relationship between $E[y_t]$ and $E[v_t]$ is discussed in a following section in the context of the estimation of these two functions.

3 See Chapter 7 Appendix for the detailed derivation.

A profit-maximizing farmer can use this relationship to determine the optimal nitrogen fertilizer application rate, a^*_t, in period t. Knowing only the initial nitrogen level in the soil, x_t, the expected crop price at harvest time, p^y_t, the expected nitrogen fertilizer price in the next period t+1, p^f_{t+1}, which is based on the current (known) fertilizer price, p^f_t, the concave expected nitrogen carry-over rate function and expected yield function, an optimal value of nitrogen available for plant uptake, r^*_t, can be computed. The optimal nitrogen fertilizer application rate, a^*_t, is determined by subtracting the initial value x_t from r^*_t. Note that the optimal nitrogen fertilizer application rate in the current period t is not affected by either the amount of carry-over nitrogen in previous periods or the prices of nitrogen fertilizer and the crop in future periods. This rule is particularly useful for nutrient management when soil N-testing is used to determine the initial nitrogen level.

THE STEADY-STATE SOLUTION FOR THE DYNAMIC ECONOMIC OPTIMIZATION MODEL

The optimal "steady-state" value of nitrogen available for plant uptake is a constant amount of nitrogen in the soil, r^*, that must be maintained at a specific time for plant uptake in order to maximize the net farm income (relationship (7.1)). It is determined by assuming that both expected prices of nitrogen fertilizer and the crop are constant and that the expected yield function and the expected nitrogen carry-over rate function are invariant over time (that is $y = y_t$ and $v = v_t$). Annual soil N-test will be needed to reveal the amount of carry-over nitrogen, x_t, for the determination of the annual amount of nitrogen to be added to maintain r^*. In the absence of a soil N-test, a farmer must exogenously determine the optimal steady-state nitrogen application rate, a^*, and apply this rate annually to maximize the net farm income.

To keep the mathematics tractable, the optimal steady-state application rate will be determined from relationship (7.5) for just two time periods, t = 1, 2. In the first period, the optimal amount of nitrogen available for plant uptake, r^*_1 (=r^*), is obtained by the solving relationship (7.5) using the initial condition, x_1. Then, the optimal nitrogen fertilizer application rate, a^*_1, at period 1 is obtained by subtracting x_1 from r^*_1. The amount of residual nitrogen expected to be carried-over from period 1 to period 2, $E[x_2]$, is $E[v(r^*)]\{r^* - k\ E[y(r^*)]\}$, which is a constant. The expected steady-state level of nitrogen carried-over, x^*, is equal to $E[x_2]$. By subtracting x^* from r^*, the steady-state optimal application rate, a^*, is

$$(7.6) \quad a^* = r^* - E[v(r^*)]\{r^* - k\ E[y(r^*)]\}$$

Thus, corresponding to a given r^* and with a constant expected yield, $E[y(r^*)]$, and a constant expected carry-over rate of nitrogen, $E[v(r^*)]$, there is an optimal steady-state fertilizer application rate, a^*.[4] By applying this amount of nitrogen fertilizer annually, a farmer, in the absence of soil N-test, will maximize the present value of expected net farm income in the long-run.

A farmer can use the steady-state solution to manage the application of nitrogen fertilizer in two ways - with or without a soil N-test - when faced with a stochastic yield function and a stochastic nitrogen carry-over rate function. With soil N-testing, the farmer can apply the additional amount of nitrogen fertilizer needed to maintain nitrogen at the optimal level, r^*. Without using a soil N-test, the farmer will annually apply nitrogen fertilizer at the optimal steady-state application rate, a^*. In this instance, the application rate will be constant since both the optimal amount of nitrogen available for plant uptake, r^*, and the nitrogen fertilizer carry-over rate, x_t, are constant over time. Theoretically, the farmer who uses the soil N-test will obtain the maximum present value of expected net farm income over the planning horizon. The farmer who does not use the soil N-test will have a smaller present value of expected net farm income than the one uses soil N-test. The reason is that the farmer who annually applies variable amounts of nitrogen fertilizer based on the results of a soil N-test can maintain the amount of nitrogen available for plant uptake at r^*. The farmer who does not use a soil N-test, however, and annually applies a constant amount of nitrogen fertilizer cannot maintain the amount of nitrogen available for plant uptake at r^* ever year.[5] Without the use of a soil N-test, the actual amount of nitrogen available for plant uptake will be larger than r^* in some years and smaller in other years, although the expected value of r is equal to r^*. Consequently, because of diminishing marginal returns of nitrogen fertilizer (Bosch et al. [1994]), the farmer who does not use soil N-testing will realize *ex post* a smaller aggregate net farm income.

Next, the corresponding expected steady-state residual nitrogen, w^*, (i.e., the amount of nitrogen fertilizer applied in excess of the amount of nitrogen removed with the harvested crop), can be calculated by the equation $w^* = a^* - k\,E[y(r^*)]$. It can be shown that w^* is the expected amount of nitrogen loss at the steady-state. As noted, for a specific field, there is an optimal value of r^* for given nitrogen fertilizer and crop prices. At the steady-state, the amount of residual nitrogen determines the amount of nitrogen loss.[6]

---

4 Taylor [1983] proves the existence of a unique value of r^*. He states that "... it is determined only for the time period for which the optimal nitrogen fertilizer application is to be determined, rather than for an arbitrarily large number of time periods typically assumed to assure convergence of the decision rule as in the standard dynamic programming model."

5 The difference in the nitrogen application rate between the situations when soil N-testing is used and when it is not used can be illustrated by a simple example: With soil N-test used, the farmer annually applies nitrogen fertilizer in the $a_t = r^* - x^* + \Lambda_t$, where x^* is the expected carry-over rate of nitrogen, and Λ_t is a the random error with zero mean and finite variance. The value of x^* can be observed when a soil N-test is used. Without a soil N-test, however, the farmer annually applies nitrogen fertilizer in the amount $a^* = r^* - x^{**}$, where $x^{**} = E(x_t)$. This latter term, $E(x_t)$, is constant over the planning horizon so that a^* is time invariant.

6 The contention that the expected amount of nitrogen loss, f, is equal to the expected amount of residual nitrogen, w^*, at the steady-state can be demonstrated in a straightforward fashion. At the steady state, $x^* = E[v(r^*)]\,\{x^* + a^* - k\,E[y(r^*)]\}$. Define expected residual nitrogen as

It is clear that the steady-state solution does not hold when unusual weather conditions such as drought occur and cause a crop failure. Under such a situation, soil N-testing must be used to detect excess nitrogen accumulation in the soil and help the farmer adjust the application rate of nitrogen fertilizer so as to maintain the amount of nitrogen available for plant uptake at r^*.

THE CROP PRODUCTION PROCESS MODEL

In order to obtain the steady-state solution for the amount of nitrogen that must be available for plant uptake, r^*, the expected yield response (production) function, E[y], and the expected nitrogen carry-over rate function, E[v], for a specific field under a given nutrient management practice must be estimated. The Erosion Productivity Impact Calculator (EPIC) can provide the requisite data for the estimation of these two functions. The EPIC model is a comprehensive crop production process model developed by USDAs Agricultural Research Service (ARS) primarily to estimate soil erosion and its impact on soil productivity in the United States (Williams et al. [1990]).[7] It has also evolved into an important tool to simulate degradation and movement of agricultural chemicals in the soil. The EPIC model is a stochastic crop production process model whereby crop growth and the fate of nitrogen, including carry-over nitrogen, are subject to the stochastic variation of daily weather. In EPIC model simulations, daily precipitation, temperature, and solar radiation are randomly generated from assumed probability distributions (Richardson and Nicks [1990]). As a consequence, annual crop yield and the nitrogen carry-over rate are stochastic functions. The crop growth component in the EPIC model generates data for the estimation of the stochastic yield response function. The yield response function must be empirically estimated since crop yields in the EPIC model are determined by a harvest index and aboveground biomass and are indirectly linked to the available nitrogen in the soil. The nutrient component in the EPIC model generates data for the estimation of the stochastic nitrogen carry-over rate function. This function is estimated by using the nitrogen mass balance framework in the nutrient component.

The nitrogen mass balance component in the EPIC model is formulated as a system of equations (Table 7.1). Inputs to crop production include commercial nitrogen applications (FN), nitrogen from precipitation (NPRCP), and nitrogen fixation (NFIX) (equation (i)). Nitrogen is removed from the system through removal of the crop harvested (YLN), subsurface flow (SSFN), percolation (PRKN), surface runoff (YNO_3),

---

$w^* = a^* - k\,E[y(r^*)]$. Then, $x^* = E[v(r^*)]\,(x^* + w^*)$, which can be expressed as $x^* = E[v(r^*)]/\{1-E[v(r^*)]\}\,w^*$. Substitute x^* into the nitrogen loss equation $\phi = (1-E[v(r^*)])\,(x^* + w^*)$. This gives $\phi = w^*$.

7 EPIC was selected over other process models such as NLEAP and CREAMS (Shaffer [1995]) because these other models do not have the crop growth component. This component is essential for estimating yield response as a function of available nitrogen as well as nutrient mass balance. The latter value is used in estimation of the carry-over rate function.

denitrification (DN), and volatilization (AVOL) (equation (ii)). The net change in nitrate (NO_3) due to transformation through mineralization of soil organic nitrogen to nitrate and immobilization of nitrate to organic nitrogen is estimated as the change in the quantity of organic nitrogen in the active pool (ORG N AC) and in the stable pool (ORG N ST) from period t to period t+1 minus all organic nitrogen loss in sediment in period t (YON) (equation (iii)). The nitrogen available for plant uptake (equation (iv)) is the initial nitrate level (NO_3) plus nitrogen inputs (equation (i)) adjusted for the organic change (equation (iii)) in the soil. The carry-over nitrate (equation (v)) in period t+1 is nitrogen available for plant uptake (equation (iv)) minus nitrogen disappearance (equation (ii)). Nitrogen available for carry-over (equation (vi)) is nitrogen available for uptake (equation (iv)) less nitrogen in the harvested crop (YLN).

The nitrogen mass balance component in the EPIC model can be validated by comparing the annual carry-over nitrogen amounts, $NO_{3(t+1)}$, estimated by equation (v) in period t with the realized annual carry-over nitrogen amount generated by the EPIC model in period t+1. The annual nitrogen carry-over rate is the ratio of equation (v) divided by equation (vi). The EPIC model generated annual carry-over rates and the corresponding amounts of nitrogen available for plant uptake are used in the estimation of the expected carry-over function.

DETERMINATION OF THE OPTIMAL NITROGEN FERTILIZER APPLICATION RATE FOR CORN GROWN AT THE ARS DEMONSTRATION FARM IN SOUTHERN MARYLAND

Use of soil N-testing can be one component of a best nutrient management practice designed to help a farmer determine the amount of nitrogen fertilizer to apply in order to maintain the optimal level of nitrogen in the soil available for plant uptake. Assuming an objective of maximizing the present value of expected farm net income, the optimal level of nitrogen that must be maintained in the soil must be determined. In what follows, this is done for corn grown at the USDAs Agricultural Research Service Sustainable Agriculture Demonstration Farm in Southern Maryland. The steps involved in this determination include EPIC model simulations, estimation of the expected yield function and expected nitrogen carry over rate function using EPIC generated data, and the application of the dynamic rule (relationship (7.5)) to determine the required optimal steady-state nitrogen level in soil available for plant uptake.

(a) EPIC Model Simulations

Version 5300 of the EPIC model was employed to simulate production of continuous corn on a hypothetical farm modeled after the Sustainable Agriculture Demonstration Farm at the USDA's Beltsville Agricultural Research Center, a 2.4 hectare site on the South Farm operated by the Agricultural Research Service. The Demonstration Farm has a complex soil with slope varying between 2 and 15 percent. In the EPIC model simulations, Sassafras soil, one of the soil types present at this site, with an 8% slope was used. Weather records from Owings Ferry Landing in southern Maryland were also used. It was assumed that corn is continuously planted since it is one of the common practices in corn production and it uses more nitrogen fertilizer per acre than any other cropping practice (Gill and Padgitt [1995]). The farmer is assumed to use PSNT annually with the soil N-test being conducted at the end of May to determine the amount of nitrogen in the soil. Based on relationship (7.5), the farmer then computes the amount of nitrogen to be applied at the beginning of June for side-dressing. In the EPIC model simulations, the farmer must apply 22.4 kilograms per hectare of nitrogen fertilizer (10-20-10) annually at the time of planting (at the beginning of April) in addition to the amount of nitrogen fertilizer (28-0-0) applied at the beginning of June that is determined based on the results of the soil N-test.

As noted previously, the EPIC model for corn was used because it has been extensively validated across a wide range of soil types and weather conditions in different parts of the United States. Rigorous statistical validation of the EPIC model for the Sustainable Agriculture Demonstration Farm, however, was limited by the lack of the requisite field-level data. Consequently, validation was based on a comparison of nitrogen fertilizer use efficiency between EPIC model simulation results and the results from actual corn production at the Demonstration Farm. A soil scientist familiar with the site was also consulted. Corn grown after soybeans at the Sustainable Agricultural Demonstration Farm produced an average yield of 11.30 mt/ha for 205 kg/ha of fertilizer nitrogen applied in 1994 (Lu and Kelly [1995]). The nitrogen use efficiency, which is the amount of nitrogen in the yield divided by the amount of nitrogen applied (Meisinger et al. [1992]) was 72 percent. In contrast an EPIC model simulation covering 20 years produced an average yield of 9.57 mt/ha from continuous corn production for the same amount of nitrogen fertilizer nitrogen applied at the Sustainable Agriculture Demonstration Farm. The nitrogen fertilizer use efficiency in this instance is 61 percent.[8] For the well known reasons, a lower nitrogen fertilizer use efficiency is expected for the continuous planting of corn than for corn in rotation with soybeans. The EPIC model simulation results show an average nitrogen loss of 15 kg/ha through leaching and an average nitrogen loss of 75 kg/ha in sediment. It was concluded that these EPIC model simulation results were within a reasonable range for that site after consultation with a soil scientist familiar with the site.

(b) Estimation of the expected yield function and the expected nitrogen carry-over rate function

The EPIC model was used to simulate continuous corn production for 20 years for each of the following levels of nitrogen fertilizer application rates: 160, 170, 180, 190,

---

8 Note that yields and nitrogen fertilizer application rates from the Demonstration Farm and from the EPIC simulations are slightly different than the average yield and application rates observed in production agriculture in Maryland. Annual corn yields in Maryland vary significantly. The average corn yield (1991-1993) was 6.2 mt/ha (U.S. Department of Agriculture [1994]). The average nitrogen fertilizer application rate was 123 kg/ha and nitrogen use efficiency was 73 percent.

200, 210, and 220 kg per hectare. Twenty years of EPIC model simulation results for each of the seven nitrogen fertilizer application rates were used in the estimation of the yield response function. In each EPIC model simulation, the annual average amount of nitrate in the soil at the end of May (determined by soil N-testing) plus the amount of nitrogen fertilizer applied determine the amount of nitrogen available for plant uptake. A Mischerlich-type functional specification with an asymptotic yield plateau was used in the estimation of the yield function. Yield is simply specified as a function of the amount of nitrogen available for plant uptake. This plateau function has been shown to describe adequately the relationship between yield response and nitrogen in the soil (Beattie and Taylor [1985] and Cerrato and Blackmer [1990]). The exact functional specification is given as $y = a_1(1 - \exp(a_2 r))$, where y is yield, r is nitrogen available for plant uptake at the end of May, and a_1 and a_2 are coefficients to be estimated. As noted previously, r is just the sum of nitrogen carried-over from the previous year plus nitrogen applied in the current year.

Results from the EPIC model simulations of the seven rates of nitrogen fertilizer application were also used to estimate the expected nitrogen carry-over rate function. The annual average carry-over rate and the annual average nitrogen available for plant uptake were used in the estimation of the expected nitrogen carry-over rate function. Annual carry-over rates were determined by the ratio of the estimated amount of nitrogen carried-over at the end of May to the amount of residual nitrogen available for carry-over from the previous year using equation (vi) in Table 7.1. A simple linear model was specified such that $v = b_1 + b_2 r$ for the expected nitrogen carry-over rate function. The variable v is the carry-over rate and r is the amount of nitrogen available for plant uptake while b_1 and b_2 are coefficients to be estimated.

Since there is some potential gain in estimation efficiency, a nonlinear seemingly unrelated regression technique was used in the estimation of the coefficients of the yield function and the carry-over rate function in deference to estimating the coefficients of the relationships individually using classical least squares techniques (Davidson and MacKinnon [1993]). Estimation results for the yield function and the carry-over rate function are given in Table 7.2.

The pseudo-R^2 (coefficient of determination) for the yield equation is 0.87 while for the nitrogen carry-over rate equation it is 0.56. Thus, the variation in nitrogen available for plant uptake explains about 87% of the total variation in yield. Although nitrogen available for plant uptake is an important factor in the EPIC model yield determination, there are other factors, such as weather and water stress conditions during the growing period that can influence yield. Variation in these factors is not explicitly reflected in any variable in the yield function and hence are captured in the unexplained residual. The results also indicate that as the amount of nitrogen in the soil available for plant uptake increases, the decline in the nitrogen carry-over rate is relatively small. This decline, however, is statistically significantly different from zero at the 5% level.

Table 7.1. Nitrogen Mass Balance

(i)	Input -- (FN_t + $NPRCP_t$ + $NFIX_t$)
(ii)	Output -- (YLN_t + $SSFN_t$ + $PRKN_t$ + DN_t + YNO_{3t} + $AVOL_t$)
(iii)	Organic N change -- (ORG N AC_{t+1} + ORG N ST_{t+1}) - (ORG N AC_t + ORG N ST_t) - YON_t
(iv)	N available for plant uptake -- ((Input + NO_{3t}) - Organic N change)
(v)	Estimated $NO_{3(t+1)}$ -- (equation (iv) - equation(ii))
(vi)	N available for carry-over -- (equation (iv) - YLN_t)

Definitions:

FN --	N fertilizer applied (kg/ha)
NPRCP --	N in precipitation (precipitation x .008) (kg/ha)
NFIX --	N fixed by legumes (kg/ha)
YLN --	N in crop yield (kg/ha)
YON --	Organic N loss in sediment (kg/ha)
SSFN --	Mineral N loss in subsurface flow (kg/ha)
PRKN --	Mineral N loss in percolate (kg/ha)
DN --	Loss by denitrification (kg/ha)
YNO_3 --	NO_3 loss in surface runoff (kg/ha)
AVOL --	Nitrogen volatilization (kg/ha)
ORG N AC --	Organic N concentration in the active pool (kg/ha)
ORG N ST --	Organic N concentration in the stable pool (kg/ha)
NO_3 --	Nitrate concentration (kg/ha) in the soil profile

Table 7.2. Estimated Coefficients on the Corn Yield Function for Continuous Planting of Corn and the Expected Nitrogen Carry-Over Function

Parameter	Estimate	"t" statistic[17]
a_1	9.6069	408.51
a_2	-0.0163	-19.52
b_1	0.9101	21.533
b_2	-0.0004	-3.023

17 In examining the statistical significance of the estimated coefficients, a simple t-test is appropriate because each observation used in the estimation represents an average value of the 20-year simulations results from the EPIC model. The average values are normally distributed as a consequence of the law of large numbers (Pfeiffer [1965]).

There is one additional interesting result from the estimation. It was assumed in developing the relationship for the optimal amount of nitrogen available for plant uptake that yield and the nitrogen carry-over rate are independent. The credibility of this assumption is confirmed in the empirical results. Using the estimated variance-covariance matrix from the nonlinear seemingly unrelated regression, one finds the covariance between the yield function and the nitrogen carry-over rate function to be less than 40% of the variance in the yield function. Moreover, there is very little gain in estimate efficiency as a consequence of using the nonlinear seemingly unrelated regression approach instead of classical least squares. A comparison of the two sets of coefficient estimates using the different estimation approaches reveals than none of the estimated coefficients differ by more than 5% and none of these differences is statistically significantly different from zero at the 5% level.

(c) Optimal Nitrogen Recommendations

Using the estimated expected yield function and the estimated expected nitrogen carry-over function in conjunction with GAMS (General Algebraic Modeling System (Brook et al. [1987])), it is possible to solve empirically the dynamic programming problem of maximizing the present value of expected net farm income (i.e., relationship (7.1)) subject to the carry-over function (i.e., relationship (7.4)) for the optimal level of nitrogen in the soil available for plant uptake and the optimal nitrogen fertilizer application rate. (Note that empirically solving relationship (7.5) will yield the same results as solving relationship (7.1) subject to relationship (7.4).) The current period and expected next-year price of nitrogen fertilizer are assumed to be equal to $0.66 per kilogram. The expected price of corn is assumed to be $108.5 per metric ton. The discount rate is assumed to be 7 percent. The optimal steady-state nitrogen level in the soil for plant uptake at the end of May is 267 kg/ha and the optimal steady-state optimal nitrogen fertilizer application rate is 180 kg/ha.[9] The results are shown in column 1 in Table 7.3. The nitrogen carry-over rate at the steady-state is 0.804.

Is the GAMS's optimal solution close to the EPIC model's optimal solution obtained when applying the nitrogen fertilizer at the optimal application rate ($a^* = 180.66$ kg/ha) annually? Theoretically, as noted previously, the optimal nitrogen fertilizer application rate from both should be identical because both assume the same expected yield and expected carry-over rate functions. Practically, since numerical algorithms are involved in the estimation and simulation processes, the values would be expected to be slightly different due to the vagaries of rounding. To see just how different they are, EPIC model simulations were conducted for different nitrogen fertilizer application rates within the range of 160 kg/ha to 220 kg/ha. Results from these EPIC model simulations show that the steady-state optimal nitrogen fertilizer application rate (180.66 kg/ha in Table 7.3) is de facto in the range of the optimal application rates that can be determined from EPIC model simulations.[10] The negligible difference between the average net farm income as

9 The optimal rate includes 22.4 kg/ha of nitrogen fertilizer applied at the time of planting.

10 The difference in net farm income under different application rates in the range is relatively small.

determined by GAMS and the EPIC model simulations indicates that the optimal nitrogen fertilizer application rate estimated by either of the two approaches can be used by the farmer who seeks to maximize the present value of expected net farm income.

Table 7.3. Results from the Dynamic and Static Rules including Results from EPIC Simulation Using the Steady-state Nitrogen Application Rate

	Dynamic rule (A)	EPIC simulation (B)	Percent Difference (B-A)/A X100	Static rule (C)	Percent Difference (C-A)/A X100
Net farm income ($/ha)[1]	814.51	820.20 (32)[2]	0.7	799.00	-1.9
Yield (ton/ha)	9.48	9.52 (.33)	0.4	9.20	-2.9
N-applied (a^*) (kg/ha)	180.66	180.66 (0)	0.0	161.48	-10.6
N-carry-over (x^*) (kg/ha)	86.91	84.06 (9)	-3.3	34.28	-60.5
N-available (r^*) (Kg/ha)	267.57	262.06 (9)	-0.2	195.76	-24.8
N-loss (w^*)[3] (kg/ha)	21.31	22.00 (5)	3.0	6.93	67.5

[1] Net farm incomes under dynamic and static rules are the steady-state undiscounted values, while net farm income under EPIC is the average undiscounted value from 17-years simulation. The values of the first three years are deleted to avoid the effect of the initial conditions.

[2] The figure in the parentheses is the standard deviation of the estimate.

[3] N-loss does not include the loss of organic N initially in the soil. Nitrogen loss from the EPIC model simulations is computed by the equation:

N-loss = PRKN + DN + SSFN + AVOL + YNO_3 + (YON - ORG-N changes).
(22 kg/ha) (3) (0) (2) (0) (2) (76) (61)

The definitions of these terms are given in Table 7.1.

Can the steady-state optimal amount of nitrogen that needs to be available for plant uptake ($r^* = 268$ kg/ha) be used to compute the optimal nitrogen fertilizer application rate recommendation based on soil N-testing? To answer this question, EPIC model simulations using nitrogen fertilizer application recommended rates ranging between 240 to 280 kg/ha based on soil N-testing were investigated. In each simulation, the EPIC model was run for one year at a time for 20 years. At the end of each year (May), a soil N-test was conducted and the test information used to determine the amount of supplemental nitrogen fertilizer that needed to be applied based on the recommended rate.[11] The EPIC model simulation results[12] indicate that the steady-state optimal nitrogen fertilizer application rate is within the range of the optimal solution. Therefore, the results of soil N-testing can credibly be used.

Finally, will it make a significant difference if, instead of the dynamic rule, the static rule, which ignores the value of carry-over nitrogen, is used to determine the recommended nitrogen fertilizer application rate? The static rule determines the optimal nitrogen application rate by equating the value of the marginal product of fertilizer to the expected fertilizer price. That is, the static rule states $\alpha E[p^y{}_t]\partial E[y_t]/\partial a_t = p^f{}_t$. (Drop the second term on the right-hand-side of equation (7.5)). By applying this rule, the optimal static "steady-state" application rate is determined. (Note the implicit assumption that the nitrogen carry-over is constant.[13]) The optimal static steady-state solution is shown in Table 7.3. A farmer adopting the static rule will use significantly less nitrogen fertilizer than one using the dynamic rule. This results in a smaller net farm income but a significantly smaller nitrogen loss.

BENEFITS AND COSTS OF SOIL N-TESTS

An important issue in the fertilizer application decision is precisely what is the benefit to the farmer (private benefit) and what is the benefit to the environment (social benefit) of soil N-testing. In what follows, these benefits will be estimated. The benefits of soil N-test are measured by the difference in net farm income (private benefit) and the difference in nitrogen loss (social benefit) between when a soil N-test is used and when no soil N-test is employed. The EPIC model is used to evaluate the benefit of soil N-testing to the profit-maximizing corn farmer under the following seven scenarios: (1) annual nitrogen fertilizer applications based on the results of soil N-testing (the

---

11 The authors are grateful to Veral Benson at the Blackland Research Center, Temple, Texas, for showing how to run EPIC when the soil N-testing is involved.

12 The simulation results are shown in scenario 1 (Benchmark scenario) in Table 7.4.

13 The optimal static 'steady-state' application rate can be determined in two iterations. First, assign an arbitrary value for initial nitrogen in the soil and solve the static rule for the optimal solution. The nitrogen carry-over function (7.4) is used to determine the amount of carry-over nitrogen for the next period. Second, with this carry-over nitrogen as an initial condition for the second time period, solve the static rule again to obtain the optimal static steady-state nitrogen carry-over level and application rate.

benchmark), (2) an annual fixed application rate (180 kg/ha) based on the correct expected nitrogen carry-over rate, (3) an annual fixed application rate based on a 20% over-estimate of the correct carry-over rate, (4) an annual fixed application rate based on a 25% under-estimate of the correct carry-over rate, (5) an annual fixed application rate based on a 50% under-estimate of the correct carry-over rate, (6) an annual application rate based on yield goals of the past three-year yield average, and (7) an annual fixed application rate based on an expected plateau-yield goal. In scenario 1, the farmer uses soil N-test results to estimate the nitrogen fertilizer application rate needed to have the optimal amount of nitrogen available for plant uptake during the growing season. In scenarios 2 to 5, the farmer systematically overestimates or underestimates the application rate. These four scenarios are designed to show that the benefits of soil N-testing to the profit-maximizing farmer depends on the farmer's knowledge about the nitrogen carry-over rate of the field. In scenario 6, the farmer uses prior yield information to determine the yield goal associated with a nitrogen fertilizer application rate. Annual application rates are based on 1.2 times the yield goal, where 1.2 is the amount of nitrogen required to produce a bushel of corn that is consistent with a yield based on the average of the yields in the previous three years.[14] In scenario 7, the farmer determines the application rate using an unbiased expected plateau-yield goal. The application rate is based on the amount of nitrogen needed to achieve an expected plateau yield.[15] Scenarios 6 and 7 compare two common rule-of-thumb nutrient management practices frequently used in the absence of soil N-testing. In each scenario, 22.4 kg/ha of nitrogen (10-20-10) of the total amount of nitrogen to be applied is applied at the time of planting at the beginning of April.

(a) Soil N-testing (Benchmark) Scenario

With soil N-testing, the farmer at period t = 1 uses soil N-testing to indicate the amount of carry-over nitrogen in the soil at the end of May before side-dressing is applied in early June. Based on the soil N-test results, supplemental nitrogen fertilizer (28-0-0) is added to the soil to maintain 268 kg/ha of nitrogen in the soil at the end of May. This is the steady-state optimal amount of nitrogen that should be available for plant uptake, as determined by the dynamic rule (relationship (7.5)). The EPIC model is run for one year at a time for 20 years. At the end of May in each crop year, a soil N-test is conducted and the test results are used to determine the amount of supplementary nitrogen fertilizer needed. A summary of the 20-years of simulation results is shown under scenario 1 in Table 7.4. The average net farm income is $816/ha (with a standard deviation of 38). Included in this is a reduction of $6/ha for the cost of soil N-testing based on Bosch et al. [1994]. The nitrogen losses from leaching sediment, denitrification, volatilization, and subsurface flow and surface runoff are also shown in Table 7.4. Total

---

14 The efficiency factor of 1.2 is typically used in calculating the nitrogen fertilizer application rate for a given corn yield (Blackmer et al [1992] and Meisinger et al. [1992]).

15 The nitrogen fertilizer application rate is estimated by 1.2 times the expected plateau yield. This is 9.607 mt/ha based on the estimated yield function (Table 7.2).

nitrogen losses (N-Loss), excluding the organic nitrogen initially in the soil, is 23.5 kg/ha (with a standard deviation of 7.9).[16]

(b) Correctly Estimating Nitrogen Carry-Over Rate Scenario

Next, assume the farmer annually applies the optimal steady-state application rate, 180 kg/ha, as determined by the dynamic rule using the correct nitrogen carry-over rate (0.804). The EPIC model simulation results are shown under scenario 2 in Table 7.4. The average annual net farm income is $820 per hectare (with a standard deviation of 33) and the average annual nitrogen loss is 23 kilograms per hectare (with a standard deviation of 8). The farmer switching to soil N-testing will lose $4/ha of net farm income, but will reduce nitrogen loss by 2 kg/ha. The tradeoff between net farm income loss and nitrogen loss reduction is an obvious dilemma posing a tradeoff for the farmer (private loss) and society (public gain).

(c) Overestimate the Nitrogen Carry-Over Rate by 20% Scenario

When the nitrogen carry-over rate is systematically overestimated by 20 percent, the farmer applies 166 kg/ha of nitrogen fertilizer annually. This is the optimal steady-state nitrogen application rate estimated by GAMS assuming a 20% overestimate of the correct nitrogen carry-over rate. This value is used as the fixed value in the EPIC model simulations. The EPIC model simulation results are shown under the scenario 3 in Table 7.4. By moving from this scenario to the benchmark (i.e., adopting soil N-testing), the farmer will loose $2/ha in net farm income and will increase nitrogen loss by 6 kg/ha. In this instance both the farmer and society are better off not using soil N-testing.

(d) Underestimate the Nitrogen Carry-Over Rate by 25% Scenario

When the nitrogen carry-over is systematically overestimated by 25 percent, the farmer applies 192 kg/ha of nitrogen fertilizer annually. The EPIC model simulation results are shown under scenario 4 in Table 7.4. Moving from this scenario to the benchmark will result in a decrease of 11 kg/ha in nitrogen loss but with no change in net farm income although there is a slight change in income variability. Under this scenario, a farmer will be unaffected but society will be better off using soil N-testing to reduce nitrogen losses.

(e) Underestimate the Nitrogen Carry-Over Rate by 50% Scenario

When the nitrogen carry-over rate is underestimated by 50 percent, the farmer applies 196 kg/ha of nitrogen fertilizer. The EPIC model simulation results are shown under scenario 5 in Table 7.4. By moving from this scenario to the benchmark, the farmer will

---

[16] The results in Table 7.5 indicate that nitrogen loss at the Sustainable Agriculture Demonstration Farm comes mainly from organic nitrogen loss via sediment (70 kg/ha/yr). This results primarily from the depletion of soil organic matter (55 kg/ha/yr) initially in the soil. Nitrogen losses from nitrate leaching, denitrification, subsurface flow, surface runoff, and volatilization are relatively small.

Table 7.4. EPIC Model Simulation Results for Various Nitrogen Fertilizer Management Scenarios

Scenarios	1	2	3	4	5	6	7
N-soil testing used	yes	no	no	no	no	no	no
Avg Application Rate	178	180	166	192	196	182	206
(FN) (kg/ha)	(22)[1]	(0)	(0)	(0)	(0)	(4)	(0)
Average Yield	9.54	9.55	9.43	9.57	9.57	9.55	9.57
(ton/ha)	(0.33)	(0.33)	(0.32)	(0.34)	(0.33)	(0.33)	(0.34)
Net Farm Income[2]	816	820	818	816	812	820	806
($/ha)	(38)[3]	(33)	(32)	(33)	(33)	(33)	(33)
Nitrogen leached	2.3	3.3	2.3	6	8	4	15
(PRKN) (kg/ha)	(2.5)	(3.3)	(2.3)	(6)	(8)	(4)	(12)
Nitrogen in sediment	70	74	72	75	75	71	75
(YON) (kg/ha)	(45)	(47)	(46)	(48)	(48)	(46)	(48)
Nitrogen denitrification	0.4	0.5	0.2	1.0	1.0	0.6	1.0
(DN) (kg/ha)	(0.5)	(0.5)	(0.3)	(0.2)	(0.2)	(0.5)	(0)
Nitrogen in subs flow	2	2.0	1.6	2.6	2.6	2.3	3.3
(SSFN) (kg/ha)	(0.6)	(0.7)	(0.7)	(0.8)	(0.8)	(0.8)	(0.9)
Nitrogen surface runoff	1.5	1.5	1.3	1.7	1.7	1.6	1.7
(YNO_3) (kg/ha)	(1.4)	(1.2)	(1.0)	(1.5)	(1.5)	(1.4)	(1.6)
Organic N depletion	55	58	62	56	54	55	54
(kg/ha)	(45)	(48)	(45)	(49)	(49)	(46)	(49)
Nitrogen Loss[4]	21	23	15	32	35	24	42
(kg/ha)	(7)	(8)	(9)	(9)	(10)	(8)	(14)

[1] Figures in parentheses are standard deviations of the estimates.
[2] The average of 20-years annual net farm income in current (undiscounted) dollars.
[3] The cost of soil N-testing is included in net farm income. It is about $6/ha.
[4] Nitrogen Loss = PRKN + DN + SSFN + YNO_3 + (YON - ORG-N change)

gain $4/ha in net farm income and also reduce nitrogen loss by 14 kg/ha. Both the farmer and society are in a win-win situation with the adoption of soil N-testing in this instance.

(f) Nitrogen Fertilizer Application Rate Based on an Average-Yield Goal Scenario

The EPIC model was run annually for 20 years to obtain the average net farm income and the average nitrogen loss based on a yield goal. The yield goal for the determination of annual nitrogen application rate is based on the average yields obtained over the previous three years. The EPIC model simulation results are shown under scenario 6 in Table 7.4. The average nitrogen fertilizer application rate is 182 kg/ha. Moving from this scenario to the N-soil testing benchmark results in a $4/ha decrease in net farm income with a corresponding contraction by 3 kg/ha in nitrogen loss. The tradeoff between the net farm income reduction and the decrease in nitrogen loss creates a dilemma that the farmer and society must confront if this scenario is adopted.

(g) Nitrogen fertilizer application rate based on an expected plateau-yield goal

Scenario

Using an expected plateau-yield goal, simulations using the EPIC model were carried out for 20 years to obtain the average annual net farm income and the average annual nitrogen loss. The annual nitrogen application rate is 206 kg/ha based on an expected maximum yield of 9.607 mt/ha. The EPIC model simulation results are shown under scenario 7 in Table 7.4. The farmer will realize an increase in net farm income of $10/ha and there will be a corresponding decrease in nitrogen loss of 21 kg/ha if this scenario is abandoned and soil N-testing adopted. The farmer and society are in a win-win situation with the adoption of soil N-testing under this scenario.

CONCLUSIONS

The economic benefits to the farmer and the environmental benefits to society associated with soil nitrogen testing by a profit-maximizing farmer depend on the farmer's knowledge about nitrogen carry-over as well as current nitrogen management practices. In the foregoing analysis, a dynamic fertilizer use decision model has been combined with a crop production process model to evaluate the economic and environmental benefits of pre-side-dress soil N-testing for a hypothetical risk-neutral farmer growing corn at the USDAs Agricultural Research Service Sustainable Agriculture Demonstration Farm site in southern Maryland. For the farmer who is knowledgeable about expected nitrogen carry-over, adoption of soil N-testing may lead to a reduction in net farm income but it may also precipitate a reduction in nitrogen losses to the environment. For the farmer currently overestimating the expected nitrogen carry-over rate by more than 20 percent, soil N-testing will not lead to a reduction in nitrogen loss but it may lead to an improvement in net farm income. For the farmer currently underestimating the expected nitrogen carry-over rate by more than 25 percent, soil N-testing will help reduce nitrogen losses and lead to an improvement in net farm income. For the farmer who uses a three-year average-yield goal to determine the annual nitrogen fertilizer application rate, use of soil N-testing will help reduce nitrogen loss but it will not result in any improvement in net farm income. Soil N-testing, however, will help the farmer who uses an expected plateau-yield goal improve net farm income and reduce nitrogen loss significantly.

While there are differences in the impact on net farm income of the various nutrient management scenarios not relying on soil N-testing relative to the benchmark which is based on soil N-testing (with the exception of scenario 7), these differences are simply too small to ensure that soil N-testing can lead to an improvement or reduction in net farm income. This is because of the relatively large fluctuations in net farm income attributable to the variability in the weather.

Use of soil N-testing does not reduce the variation (standard deviations) in net farm income and nitrogen loss. This is highlighted in Table 7.4. If the farmer is risk-averse, the soil N-testing will not mitigate the variability in net farm income. The small differences in net farm income and in the variation in net farm income as measured by the standard deviation across scenarios can be explained by the fact that the weather conditions during the growing season have a stronger effect on crop yield than any differences in the amount of nitrogen fertilizer applied. Thus, the results from this study do not support the argument that there are unequivocal positive benefits from using soil N-testing for either the farmer or society.

Finally, the results do suggest that soil N-testing is a valuable tool that can be used to improve net farm income and reduce nitrogen loss for the farmer currently applying nitrogen fertilizer based on an expected plateau-yield goal. The results suggest that soil N-testing can be beneficial to the farmer by leading to an enhancement in net farm income and to society by leading to reduced nitrogen loss if the farmer has underestimated the nitrogen carry-over rate by more than 25 percent. If soil N-testing is to be a useful tool to improve water quality in the study area, farmers underestimating nitrogen carry-over rate by more than 25% should be targeted. If soil N-testing is to be promoted as an important method in reducing nonpoint source pollution in the nation, a procedure to identify these farmers in the win-win situation through, for example, surveys to assess field-level nitrogen mass balance and the use of the evaluation method presented in this study will have to be developed.

REFERENCES

Agricultural Statistics, U.S. Department of Agriculture, U.S. Government Printing Office, Washington, DC, 1994.

Babcock, B., "The Effects of Uncertainty on Optimal Nitrogen Applications," *Review of Agricultural Economics*, Vol. 14 (1992), pp. 271-280.

Babcock, B. and A. Blackmer, "The Value of Reducing Temporal Input Non-Uniformities," *Journal of Agricultural and Resource Economics*, Vol. 17(1992), pp. 335-347.

Beattie, B. and C. Taylor, *The Economics of Production*, John Wiley and Sons, New York, NY, 1985.

Blackmer, A., "Losses and Transport of Nitrogen from Soil," in *Rural Groundwater Contamination*, edited by F. D'Itri and L. Wolfson, Lewis Publishers, Inc., Chelsea, MI, 1987.

Blackmer, A., T. Morris, and G. Binford, "Predicting N Fertilizer Needs for Corn in Humid Regions: Advances in Iowa," in *Predicting N Fertilizer Needs for Corn in Humid Regions*, edited by B. Bock and K. Kelley, Bulletin Y-226, National Fertilizer and Environmental Research Center, Tennessee Valley Authority, Muscle Shoals, AL, 1992.

Bock, B., K. Kelley, and J. Meisinger, "Predicting N Fertilizer Needs in Humid Regions: Summary and Future Directions," in *Predicting N Fertilizer Needs for Corn in Humid Regions*, edited by B. Bock and K. Kelley, Bulletin Y-226, National Fertilizer and Environmental Research Center, Tennessee Valley Authority, Muscle Shoals, AL, 1992.

Bosch, D., K. Fuglie, and R. Keim, *Economic and Environmental Effects of Nitrogen Testing for Fertilizer Management*, Staff Report No. AGES9413. Resources and Technology Division, Economic Research Service, U.S. Department of Agriculture, Washington, DC, 1994.

Brooke, T., D. Kendrick and A. Meeraus, *GAMS: A User's Guide*, Scientific Press, South San Francisco, CA, 1987.

Cerrato, M. and A. Blackmer, "Comparison of Models for Describing Corn Yield Response to Nitrogen Fertilizer," *Agronomy Journal*, Vol. 82 (1990), pp. 138-142.

Davidson, R., and J. Mackinnon, *Estimation and Inference in Econometrics*, Oxford University Press, Oxford, 1993.

Frank, M., B., and M. Embleton, "A Comparison of Alternative Crop Response Models," *American Journal of Agricultural Economics*, Vol. 72 (1990), pp. 597-603.

Fuglie, K. and D. Bosch, "Economic and Environmental Implications of Soil Nitrogen Testing: A Switching-Regression Analysis," *American Journal of Agricultural Economics*, Vol. 77 (1995), pp. 891-900.

Gill, M. and M. Padgitt, *AREI UPDATES: Cropping Patterns*, NRED Number 18, Economic Research Service, U.S. Department of Agriculture, Washington, DC, 1995.

Huang, W., D. Shank, and T. Hewitt, "On-Farm Costs of Reducing Residual Nitrogen on Cropland Vulnerable to Nitrate Leaching," *Review of Agricultural Economic*, Vol. 18 (1996), pp. 325-339.

Kelly, T., Y. Lu, and J. Teasdale, "Economic-Environmental Tradeoffs Among Alternative Crop Rotations," *Agriculture, Ecosystems and Environment*, Vol. 60 (1996), pp. 17-28.

Kennedy, J., "Rules for Optimal Fertilizer Carryover," *Review of Marketing and Agricultural Economics*, Vol. 54 (1986), pp. 3-10.

Kitur, B., M. Smith, R. Blevins, and W. Frye, "Fate of N-Deleted Ammonium Nitrate Applied to No-Tillage and Conservation Tillage Corn," *Agronomy Journal*, Vol. 76 (1984), pp. 240-242.

Kleijnen, J., *Statistical Tools for Simulation Practitioners*, Marcel Deckker, Inc., New York, NY, 1987.

Lu, Y. and T. Kelly, "Economic Analysis of Alternative Cropping Rotations at the Sustainable Agriculture Demonstration for 1994," Unpublished report, Agricultural Research Service, U.S. Department of Agriculture, Beltsville, MD, 1995.

Meisinger, J., V. Randall, G. Stanford, and J. Legg, "Nitrogen Utilization of Corn Under Minimum Tillage and Moldboard Plow Tillage, Four-Year Results Using Labeled Fertilizer on an Atlantic Coastal Plain Soil," *Agronomy Journal*, Vol. 77 (1985), pp. 602-611.

Meisinger, J., F. Magdoff, and J. Schepers, "Predicting N Fertilizer Needs for Corn in Humid Regions: Underlying Principles," in *Predicting N Fertilizer Needs for Corn in Humid Regions*, edited by B. Bock and K. Kelley, Bulletin Y-226, National Fertilizer and Environmental Research Center, Tennessee Valley Authority, Muscle Shoals, AL, 1992.

National Research Council, *Alternative Agriculture*, National Academy Press, Washington, DC, 1989.

Olson, R., "Fate of Tagged Nitrogen Fertilizer Applied to Irrigated Corn," *American Journal of Soil Science Society*, Vol. 44 (1980), pp. 514-517.

Pfeiffer, P., *Concepts of Probability Theory*, McGraw-Hill Book Company, New York, NY, 1965.

Richardson, C. and A. Nicks, "Weather Generator Description," in *EPIC-Erosion/Productivity Impact Calculator, Volume 1, Model Documentation*, Technical Bulletin Number 1768, Agricultural Research Service, U.S. Department of Agriculture, Temple, TX, 1990.

Segarra, E., D. Ethridge, C. Deussen, and A. Onken, "Nitrogen Carry-Over Impacts in Irrigated Cotton Production, Southern High Plains of Texas," *Western Journal of Agricultural Economics*, Vol. 14 (1989), pp. 300-309.

Shaffer, M., "Fate and Transport of Nitrogen: What Models Can and Cannot Do," Working Paper No. 11, The RCA III, Natural Resources Conservation Service, U.S. Department of Agriculture, Washington, DC, 1995.

Shaffer, M., A. Halvorson, and F. Pierce, "Nitrate Leaching and Economic Analysis Package (NLEAP): Model Description and Application," in *Managing Nitrogen for Groundwater and Profitability*, edited by R. Follett et al., Soil Science Society of America, Madison, WI, 1990.

Shortle, J., W. Musser, W. Huang, B. Roach, K. Kreahling, D. Beegle, and R. Fox, *Economic and Environmental Potential of the Pre-Side-Dressing Soil Nitrate Test*, Final Report to the Environmental Protection Agency, Department of Agricultural Economics and Rural Sociology, Pennsylvania State University, University Park, PA, 1993.

Taylor, C., "Certainty Equivalence for Determination of Optimal Fertilizer Application Rates with Carry-over," *Western Journal of Agricultural Economics*, Vol. 8 (1983), pp. 85-97.

U.S. Department of Agriculture, *EPIC-Erosion/Productivity Impact Calculator*, Agricultural Research Service, U.S. Department of Agriculture, Temple, TX, 1990.

U.S. Environmental Protection Agency, *National Survey of Pesticides in Drinking Water Wells, Phase I report*, EPA 570/9-90-015, U.S. Environmental Protection Agency, Washington, DC, 1990.

U.S. Environmental Protection Agency, Office of Water, *Guidance Specifying Management Measures for Sources of Nonpoint Pollution on Coastal Waters*, 840-B-92-002, Washington, DC, 1993.

Williams, J., P. Dyke, W. Fuchs, V. Benson, O. Rice, and E. Taylor, *EPIC-Erosion/Productivity Impact Calculator: User's Manual*, Agricultural Research Service, U.S. Department of Agriculture, Temple, TX, 1990.

Williams, J., and D. Krissel, "Water Percolation: An Indicator of N Leaching Potential," in *Managing Nitrogen for Groundwater Quality and Farm Profitability*, edited by R. Follett, Soil Science Society of America, Madison, WI, 1990.

CHAPTER 7 APPENDIX

Derivation of the Stochastic Rule for the Optimal Nitrogen Fertilizer Application Rate

The derivation of the stochastic rule for the optimal nitrogen fertilizer application rate follows Kennedy's direct dynamic programming method. The crop yield response in period t is $y_t(r_t,\delta_t)$ where r_t is nitrogen available for plant uptake in period t and δ_t is a random variable. The percent of residual nitrogen to be carried-over from period t to t+1, v_t, is given as $v_t(w_t,r_t,\varepsilon_t)$ where w_t is a site-specific variable and e_t is a random variable. The problem is to maximize the expected net farm income

(7A.1)

$$\text{Max}_{a_1 \dots a_n} \sum_{t=1}^{n} \alpha^{t-1} \, E\,[\alpha P_t^y \, y_t(r_t,\delta_t)) - p_t^f \, a_t\,]$$

subject to

(7A.2)

$$r_t = x_t + a_t$$

$$x_{t+1} = v_t(r_t, w_t, \varepsilon_t)(r_t - \kappa \, y_t(r_t,\delta_t))$$

$$a_t \geq 0$$

$$\text{with } x_1 \text{ given}$$

The recursive equation of the dynamic programming problem (7A.1) and (7A.2) is
(7A.3)

$$\zeta_t\{x_t, p_t^y, p_t^f\} = \text{Max}_{a_t} E[\alpha\, p_t^y\, y_t(r_t, \delta_t) - p_t^f\, a_t$$
$$+\alpha\zeta_{t+1}\{x_{t+1}, p_{t+1}^y, p_{t+1}^f\}] \quad for\ t = n, \ldots, 1$$

subject to
(7A.4)

$$r_t = x_t + a_t$$
$$x_{t+1} = v_t(r_t, w_t, \varepsilon_t)(r_t - \kappa\, y_t(r_t, \delta_t))$$
$$a_t \geq 0$$

with
(7A.5)

$$x_1\ given$$
$$\zeta_{n+1}\{x_{n+1}, p_{n+1}^y, p_{t+1}^f\} = 0$$

The dynamic programming problem (7A.3), (7A.4), and (7A.5) also can be expressed as
(7A.6)

$$\zeta_t\{x_t, p_t^y, p_t^f\} = \alpha E[p_t^y\, y_t(x_t + a_{\bar{t}}, \delta_t) - p_t^f a_t^*]$$
$$+\alpha\zeta_{t+1}\{E[x_{t+1}, p_{t+1}^y, p_{t+1}^f]\}$$

$$for\ t = 1, \ldots, n$$
$$where\ a_1^* \ldots a_n^*\ are\ the\ optimal\ rates$$

where $x_{t+1} = v_t(x_t + a^*_t - k\, y(x_t + a^*_{t}, d_t))$.

Assuming that function (7A.3) is concave, partial differentiation of (7A.3) with respect to a_t gives the first order condition for an interior maximum. This is given as
(7A.7)

$$\alpha E[p_t^y]\partial E[y_t(x_t, \delta_t)]/\partial a_t - p_t^f$$
$$+\alpha E[(\partial x_{t+1}/\partial a_t)(\partial\zeta_{t+1}/\partial x_{t+1})] = 0$$
$$for\ t = 1, \ldots, n$$

Next, partial differentiation of (7A.3) with respect to x_t gives
(7A.8)

$$\partial\zeta_t/\partial x_t = \alpha E[p_t^y]\partial E[y_t(r_t, \delta_t)]/\partial a_t$$
$$+\alpha E[(\partial x_{t+1}/\partial a_t)(\partial\zeta_{t+1}/\partial x_{t+1})]$$
$$for\ t = 1, \ldots, n$$

where $\partial y_t/\partial a_t$ is evaluated at $x_t + a^*_t$. Since the terms on the right hand side of equation (7A.8) equal p^f_t as shown in equation (7A.7), equation (7A.8) becomes

(7A.9) $$\partial \zeta_t/\partial x_t = p^f_t .$$

Substituting p^f_{t+1} for $\partial z_{t+1}/\partial x_{t+1}$, and $v_t(w_t,\varepsilon_t)(r_t-ky_t(r_t,\delta_t))$ for x_{t+1} in equation (7A.7) gives

(7A.10)

$$\alpha E[\,p^y_t\,]\partial E[\,Y_t(n_t,\delta_t\,)]/\partial\, a_t =$$
$$p^f_t - \alpha E[\,\partial\, v_t(\,r_t,w_t,\varepsilon_t\,)(\,r_t - k\,y_t(\,n_t,\varepsilon_t\,))]/\partial\, a_t\, p^f_{t+1}]$$
$$for\; t = 1,\ldots,n$$

Now, assume that the price of nitrogen fertilizer and the nitrogen carry-over rate are independent, and that the current nitrogen fertilizer price is known and that the future nitrogen fertilizer price is a random variable conditional on the price from the previous year. Given these assumptions, for a specific field (drop w_t because it is fixed), equation (7A.10) becomes

(7A.11)

$$\alpha E[\,p^y_t\,]\,\partial E[\,y_t(\,r_t,\delta_t\,)]/\partial\, a_t =$$
$$p^f_t - \alpha\partial(E[\,v_t(\,r_t,\varepsilon_t\,)]\,(\,r_t - kE[\,y_t(\,r_t,\delta_t\,)]))/\partial\, a_t\, E[\,p^f_{t+1} \mid p^f_t\,]$$
$$for\; t = 1,\ldots,n$$

With the assumption of independence between the nitrogen carry-over rate and residual nitrogen, equation (7A.11) becomes

(7A.12)

$$\alpha E[\,p^y_t\,]\,\partial E[\,y_t(\,r_t,\delta_t\,)]/\partial\, a_t =$$
$$p^f_t - \alpha\partial(E[\,v_t(\,r_t,\varepsilon_t\,)]\,(\,r_t - kE[\,y_t(\,r_t,\delta_t\,)]))/\partial\, a_t\, E[\,p^f_{t+1} \mid p^f_t\,]$$
$$for\; t = 1,\ldots,n$$

For t = 1, the optimal amount of nitrogen available for plant uptake, r^*_t, can be determined from equation (7A.12) and the optimal nitrogen fertilizer application rate, a^*_t, is the difference between r^*_t and the given initial amount of nitrogen in the soil, x_t.

Chapter 8

USING INSURANCE TO ENHANCE NITROGEN FERTILIZER APPLICATION TIMING TO REDUCE NITROGEN LOSSES TO THE ENVIRONMENT

INTRODUCTION

Agricultural use of chemical and organic nitrogen (N) fertilizers is a major contributor of nonpoint source pollutants leading to a variety of water quality problems in the United States. Agricultural use has been a major source of nitrogen for contaminating ground water through leaching, threatening the safety of rural drinking water (Phipps and Crosson [1986], Nielsen and Lee [1987], and U.S. Environmental Protection Agency [1990]). It also has become a major source for eutrophication in streams, rivers, and lakes through runoff thereby affecting ecosystems and biodiversity (Hallberg [1989] and National Research Council [1989]). To mitigate these problems, the Federal government has made available a variety of voluntary cost-sharing programs to the farmer to entice him (her) to adopt best nitrogen management practices (Federal Agriculture Improvement and Reform Act (FAIR) [1996]). Additionally, a variety of public policies have been proposed recently to help farmers to improve N use efficiency to reduce N losses to the environment (e.g., Clean Water Action Plan [1998]).

There are variety of best nitrogen management practices (BNMPs) available to a farmer to improve crops' N-use efficiency and thus reduce residual N. Adoption of a BNMP will increase his (her) farming profitability (expected net farm income) over time (Huang [1997]). One of these BNMPs is the practice of timing N fertilizer application to coincide with a plant's need. When nitrogen fertilizer application is timed to the biological needs of a crop, excessive application of N can be avoided so less residual nitrogen is available for loss to the environment. A split or a single application during the growing season can match N supply to the crop's need without a reduction in yield and can be the least cost practice associated with the application of N fertilizer. Many farmers in the United States already have adopted such a timing practice, but a substantial number have yet to follow suit (Taylor [1997]).

Possible income loss caused by adverse weather conditions is a major reason discouraging farmers from more extensively adopting a BNMP. A farmer may suffer an income loss for failing to apply N during the growing season because of unfavorable weather conditions thereby prohibiting the farmer from entering the field to apply N for optimal yield. The cost of bearing this income risk (i.e., potential loss in annual net farm income) may be so large (or, at least, be perceived to be so large) that adoption of a BNMP many not improve the certainty equivalent (CE) net income when this risk cost is included (Huang, Hewett, and Shank [1998]). Furthermore, even though adoption of a BNMP can improve the CE net income, the possibility of income losses in some years may not be acceptable to a risk-averse farmer who needs to maintain a certain level of net farm income annually. Research has found that farmers generally are risk averse (e.g. Wilson and Eidman [1983] and Tauer [1986]). To motivate risk-averse farmers to adopt a better timing approach to N fertilizer application, different approaches that reduce the real or perceived risk cost must be implemented. Insurance can be a useful tool for this purpose.

An insurance program can reduce the adoption risk cost by transferring the risk and therefore sharing risk among the participants in the program. For a specified premium, an insurance program can transfer risk from one individual (farmer) to another more able or willing to bear it or to someone (an insurance company) for whom the bearing of risk is less costly. An insurance program also can allow an individual (farmer) to share the risk by dividing it among several individuals (risk pooling) in order to reduce an individual's risk cost (Newbery and Stigliz [1985]). By risk sharing, an insurance company can lower risk cost to each participating farmer and enable individual farmers to adopt risky N fertilizer management practices which they would not otherwise implement. Therefore, it is possible for a farmer and an insurance company to have an incentive to develop an adoption insurance program to benefit both the farmer and the insurance company - a Pareto optimal move to increase social net return and to improve environmental quality .

The objective of this chapter is to explore the potential for using insurance to promote the adoption of a N fertilizer management practice to apply N fertilizer at the time of crop need to reduce N losses to the environment. In what follows, expected value-variance (EV) analysis is used to show how insurance can reduce a farmer's cost of bearing adoption risk and hence improve the farmer's CE net return after adoption of a BNMP. The adoption of growing-season only N fertilizer application in Iowa is then used as a case study to illustrate the potential gains of using insurance to promote the adoption of a BNMP to reduce N fertilizer use.

WHY ADOPTION INSURANCE?

An analytical framework is employed to demonstrate how insurance can be used to increase a farmer's incentive to adopt a BNMP. The BNMP considered will be the application of N fertilizer only during the growing season. A farmer's decision to adopt is based on the maximization of his (her) expected utility of net return. With this approach a farmer will adopt a BNMP (τ) from the currently available N management practices if such an adoption results in a greater expected utility of net farm income (net return) than using an alternative practice.

For this chapter the maximization of expected utility is formulated as the maximization of EV of net farm income (net return). (Note that for a discussion of the validity of an EV formulation, see Anderson, Dillon, and Hardaker [1977], Robison and Barry [1987], and Newbery and Stigliz [1981]). A risk-neutral farmer will select τ from available alternative practices, which maximizes expected net return $E[\pi(\tau)]$ with respect to the amount of N fertilizer applied. That is, τ will be chosen so that Max $E[U(\pi(\tau)]$ = Max $E[\pi(\tau)]$. A risk-averse farmer will select a τ which maximizes the certainty-equivalent (CE) net return with respect to N fertilizer applied. That is, for a risk-averse farmer, τ will be chosen so that Max $E[U(\pi(\tau)]$ = Max $CE(\tau)$.

Let τ^a be the baseline N management practice, such as applying all N fertilizer before planting, currently used by the farmer. This practice uses N inefficiently in crop production. Let τ^b be a best N management practice, such as applying all (or most of) N fertilizer after planting, which the policy maker would like to encourage the farmer to adopt. Let p be the probability that the adoption of τ^a fails to yield an expected return due to adverse weather conditions and results in a lower than expected net return $E[\pi(\tau^b]_f$, and let 1-p be the probability that the adoption is successful and yields an expected net return of $E[\pi(\tau^b)]_s$. The expected net return for the adoption of τ^b, the best N management practice is

$$(8.1) \quad E[\pi(\tau^b)] = (1\text{-}p)\ \{E[\pi(\tau^b)\}_s + p\ \{E[\pi(\tau^b)]_f\}$$

and the variance of the net return is (Robinson and Barry [1987])

$$(8.2) \quad Var[(\tau^b)] = p\ (1\text{-}p)\ \{E[\tau\pi(\tau^b)]_s - E[\pi(\tau^b)]_f\}^2$$

When insurance for the adoption of a BNMP is not available, a risk-neutral farmer would have an incentive to switch the N management practice from the current practice τ^a to a BNMP practice τ^b if

$$(8.3) \quad \text{Max } E[\pi(\tau^b)] \geq \text{Max } E[\pi(\tau^a)]$$

where Max $E[\pi(\tau^b)]$ is the maximum expected net return that can be obtained from the adoption of τ^b with respect to the amount of N fertilizer applied. This will be called the expected net return of adopting τ^b. A risk-averse farmer has an incentive to switch practices from τ^a to τ^b if and only if the maximum CE net return ($CE(\tau^b)$) from the adoption of τ^b with respect to the amount of N applied is greater than the maximum CE net return from τ^a ($CE(\tau^a)$). That is, a risk-averse farmer has incentive to switch practices from τ^a to τ^b if and only if

$$(8.4) \quad \text{Max } \{[E[\pi(\tau^b)] - \lambda/2 \text{ Var } (\pi(\tau^b))\} \geq \text{Max } \{[E[\pi(\tau^a)] - \lambda/2 \text{ Var } (\pi(\tau^a))\}$$

where the terms on the right-hand-side of inequality (8.4) equal $CE(\tau^b)$ and the terms on the left-hand-side equal $CE(\tau^a)$. λ is an assumed absolute risk aversion coefficient, Var $(\pi(\tau^b))$ and Var $(\pi(\tau^a)\ )$ are, respectively, the variance of the net return of τ^b and τ^a, and $\lambda/2\ Var(\pi(\tau^b))$ and $\lambda/2\ Var(\pi(\tau^a))$ are the corresponding risk costs (premiums) (Robison and Barry [1987]), or the costs of bearing the risk by the farmer (Newbery and Stigliz [1981]). When (8.4) holds, insurance may not be needed to provide the farmer with an incentive to adopt τ^b.

When inequality (8.4) is violated, that is, when $CE(\tau^b)$ is less than $CE(\tau^a)$, a risk-averse farmer will have no incentive to adopt τ^b. Insurance, however, can be used to increase $CE(\tau^b)$ by increasing the expected net return of τ^b and by reducing its risk cost to ensure that inequality (4) holds and thereby providing the farmer with the requisite incentive to adopt τ^b.

To design such an adoption insurance program would result in reducing the risk cost to R so that relationship (8.4) becomes[1]

$$(8.5) \text{ Max } E[\pi(\tau^b)] - R \geq \text{Max}\{[E[\pi(\tau^a)] - \lambda/2 \text{ Var } (\pi(\tau^a))\} \\ \geq CE(\tau^a)$$

Inequality (8.5) states that the farmer would have an incentive to adopt τ^b when he (she) expects the net return from τ^b after paying the risk cost for insurance, R, to be greater than $CE(\tau^a)$.

---

1 The terms on the left-hand-side of inequality (8.5) imply that in the presence of insurance for a farmer to reduce his (her) risk cost, a risk-averse farmer will behave as if he (she) is risk neutral in allocating input use to maximize expected net return. This is possible under the assumption of a competitive insurance market equilibrium (Rothschid and Stiglitz [1976], Ahsan, Ali, and Kurian [1982], and Nelson and Loehman [1987]). With market equilibrium, the insurer charges the insured an actuarially sound premium for the full coverage of possible loss. This probably will not *de facto* occur, however, because of the administrative and transaction costs of insurance reflected in the premium. The government can offer a subsidy to reduce the insurance premium to help a risk-averse farmer eliminate the risk costs so that the farmer would behave like a risk neutral farmer.

As noted, satisfying inequality (8.5) can be achieved by using insurance. Insurance performs two functions in reducing a farmer's adoption risk, R: (1) it transfers risk from one individual (farmer) to another (e.g., an insurance company) more able or willing to bear it, and (2) it shares risk among several individuals (farmers) to reduce the risk faced by each individual (Newbery and Stiglitz [1985]). These two functions enable an insurance company to offer an insurance policy aimed at reducing a farmer's risk cost.

Next, it is demonstrated how insurance can be used to reduce a farmer's risk cost so that the farmer will have an incentive to purchase insurance associated with the adoption of a BUMP, τ^b and how insurance can increase the CE net return associated with the adoption of τ^b so that the farmer will have an incentive to switch production practices from his (her) current baseline practice τ^a to τ^b. It is assumed that Max $E[\pi(\tau^b)]_s$ and Max $E[\pi(\tau^b)]_f$ for a given p can be determined. Let r = Max $E[\pi(\tau^b)]_s$ - Max $E[\pi(\tau^b)]_f$. Without insurance the CE net return of τ^b is (Robison and Barry [1987])

$$(8.6) \qquad CE(\tau^b)_o = \text{Max } E[\pi(\tau^b)] - \lambda/2 \; p \; (1\text{-}p) \; (r)^2$$

where Max $E[\pi(\tau^b)]$ = (1-p) Max $E[\pi(\tau^b)]_s$ + p Max $E[\pi(\tau^b)]_f$. Substituting this for Max $E[\pi(\tau^b)]$ in equation (8.6) and rearranging terms, equation (8.6) becomes[2]

$$(8.7) \qquad CE(\tau^b)_o = \text{Max } E[\pi(\tau^b)]_s - [p\, r + \lambda/2 \; p \; (1\text{-}p) \; (r)^2].$$

With insurance the farmer's CE net return of τ^b is (as shown in inequality (8.5))

$$(8.8) \qquad CE(\tau^b)_i = \text{Max } E[\pi(\tau^b)] - R$$

This can also can be expressed as

$$(8.9) \qquad CE(\tau^b)_i = \text{Max } E[\pi(\tau^b)]_s - [\, p\, r + R]$$

assuming that the farmer desires to pay insurance premium p r + R for indemnity r = (Max $E[\pi(\tau^b)]_s$ - Max $E[\pi(\tau^b)]_f$) for full coverage of potential losses. If the farmer is to have an incentive to purchase BNMP adoption insurance, R in equation (8.9) must be less than $[\lambda/2 \; p \; (1\text{-}p) \; (r)^2]$ in equation (8.7) so that $CE(\tau^b)_i$ is larger than $CE(\tau^b)_o$. This is possible through insurance.

Robison and Barry [1987] have shown that if there are n (n > 1) independent and identical farmers participating in an insurance program, it is possible for an insurance company to offer an insurance premium β_i to the farmer, with reduced risk costs (R). To

---

[2]
$$\begin{aligned}\text{Max } E[\pi(\tau^b)] &= (1\text{-}p) \text{ Max } E[\pi(\tau^b)]_s + p \text{ Max } E[\pi(\tau^b)]_f \\ &= \text{Max } E[\pi(\tau^b)]_s - p\,\{\text{Max } E[\pi(\tau^b)]_s - \text{Max } E[\pi(\tau^b)]_f\} \\ &= \text{Max } E[\pi(\tau^b)]_s - p\, r\end{aligned}$$

demonstrate this and for ease of exposition, assume no cost for the administration of the program. The insurance premium will be

(8.10) $\beta_i = p\,r + \lambda/2\, p\,(1-p)\,(r^2/n)$

for the farmer who purchases BNMP adoption insurance. In this situation the reduced risk cost is

(8.11) $R = \lambda/2\, p\,(1-p)\,(r^2/n)$

and equation (8.9) becomes

(8.12) $CE(\tau^b)_i = \text{Max } E[\pi(\tau^b)]_s - [\,p\,r + \lambda/2\, p\,(1-p)\,(r^2/n)].$

For n larger than 1, the reduced risk cost with insurance (R) is smaller than the risk cost without insurance ($\lambda/2\, p\,(1-p)\,(r)^2$ in equation (8.7)).[3] This implies that

(8.13) $CE(\tau^b)_i > CE(\tau^b)_o.$

This result means that insurance can be used to reduce the risk cost to increase a farmer's CE net return, providing an incentive for the farmer to adopt BNMP τ^b even though there is no incentive for the farmer to do so when insurance is unavailable (i.e., when inequality (8.4) is violated).

Furthermore, for the farmer to have incentive to switch production practice from the current (baseline) practice τ^a to BNMP τ^b, its CE net return, $CE(\tau^b)_i$, must be greater than the CE net return of τ^a, $CE(\tau^a)$. That is, inequality (8.5) must be satisfied. Substituting R (from equation (8.11)) into inequality (8.5), one must have

(8.14) $\text{Max } E[\pi(\tau^b)] - \{\lambda/2\, p\,(1-p)\,(r^2/n)\} > CE(\tau^a)$

This condition can be satisfied when the expected net return of τ^b, Max $E[\pi(\tau^b)]$, is greater than the certainty equivalent net return of τ^a, $CE(\tau^a)$, and then an insurance company can lower $\{\lambda/2\, p(1-p)\,(r^2/n)\}$ by increasing the number of insured farmers, n.

Inequalities (8.13) and (8.14) are two important conditions that must be satisfied for an insurance program to be a useful tool to promote the adoption of the BNMP τ^b. First, an insurance program must be able to guarantee that the CE net return of the adoption must be greater with insurance than without it. Second, an insurance program must be able to ensure that the CE net return of adoption must be greater than the CE net return of the baseline practice. For these two inequalities to hold, the expected net return of τ^b has to be greater than the CE net return of τ^a. This is an important condition to determine whether an insurance strategy can be useful to promote the adoption of a BMNP.

[3] Furthermore, R = 0 if a competitive insurance equilibrium is realized (Ahsan, Ali, and Kurian [1982]).

A MODEL FOR DEVELOPING AN INSURANCE PROGRAM

Adoption of the BNMP of applying N fertilizer only during the growing-season to meet crop needs, τ^b, is used to illustrate the efficacy of an insurance program to increase a farmer's adoption incentive. It is assumed that the farmer is currently using an inefficient N fertilizer use practice which applies all N fertilizer before planting, τ^a. Two models - an insurance purchase decision model and a production decision model for timing N fertilizer application are used.

The insurance purchase decision model is used to determine the insurance premium for a given level of indemnity. A profit-maximizing farmer, currently applying all N fertilizer in the Spring before planting, evaluates a growing-season-only application of N fertilizer to reduce N fertilizer use. The farmer is given an insurance option to protect against the possibility of income (yield) loss from failing to apply N fertilizer during the growing season because of adverse weather conditions. The farmer must determine the maximum insurance premium β_f he (she) can pay without reducing the certainty equivalent net return below the level attained with no insurance coverage. The decision matrix shown in Table 8.1 can be used to find the β_f the farmer is willing pay to maintain a certainty equivalent net return. The states of nature are (1) fail to apply N fertilizer during the growing season, s1 and (2) able to apply N fertilizer during the growing season, s2. The choices are (1) to buy insurance, a1 and (2) remain uninsured, a2. If the farmer purchases insurance, a1, the outcome in both states s1 and s2 is the certain net return which is the sum of net return loss r and the value of risk-free asset w less the insurance premium β_f. The risk-free asset w is the net return from crop production when the farmer fails to apply N fertilizer during the growing season. It is determined by the cropland's latent productivity in the absence of N fertilizer application. The value of the risk free asset w is Max $E[\pi(\tau^b)]_f$ and is known to the farmer. If the farmer is able to apply N fertilizer during the growing season, the farmer's wealth will be reduced by the risk premium β_f. If the farmer fails to apply N fertilizer, the reduction in wealth will be the sum of the insurance premium β_f and r. But the insurance company will replace the wealth lost by indemnity r to restore the farmer's net return to $(r + w - \beta_f)$ - the state of being able to apply N fertilizer. If the farmer adopts τ^b and insures the loss of net return due to the failure to apply N fertilizer, then r is Max $E[\pi(\tau^b)]_s$ - Max $E[\pi(\tau^b)]_f$. The CE net return with the insurance program becomes Max $E[\pi(\tau^b)]_s - \beta_f$, which must be greater than $CE(\tau^a)$.

If the farmer selects no insurance, choice a2, the outcome will vary with the state of nature. If the farmer fails to apply N during the growing season, the farmer's net return will be w. If farmer is able to apply N fertilizer, however, the net return will be higher with choice a2 - that is, $r + w$ versus $r + w - \beta_f$ for the insured farmer.

Table 8.1. Decision Matrix for Insurance versus No Insurance for a Growing-season-only N Fertilizer Application

State of Nature		Probability	Choices a1 Insurance	 a2 No insurance
s1	fail to apply N fertilizer during growing season	p	$r + w - \beta_f$	w
s2	able to apply N fertilizer during growing season	(1 - p)	$r + w - \beta_f$	r + w

Using the information in Table 8.1, the maximum insurance premium β_f^m that the farmer would be willingly to pay for an indemnity r to cover the possible loss of net return is (Robison and Barry, 1987)

(8.15) $\beta_f^m = p\,r + \lambda/2\, p\,(1\text{-}p)\, r^2.$

The farmer will improve his (her) CE net return if the insurance premium is less than β_f^m. An insurance company can offer insurance with a premium β_i less than β_f^m because the company is able to absorb some of the risk by facilitating risk-sharing among insured farmers. For an insurance company, the variability of the risk outcome is less than that for an individual farmer because of risk sharing (risk pooling). If the insurance company deals with n farmers with identical and independent risks, the insurance company can offer a farmer an actuarially sound insurance premium β_i such that

(8.16) $p\,r + A \leq \beta_i \leq p\,r + \lambda/2\ \mathrm{Var}(r) + A.$

where $\mathrm{Var}(r) = p\ (1\text{-}p)\ r^2/n$ and A is the cost of administrating a farmer's insurance contract.[4] If A is much smaller than the risk cost, β_i (for $n > 2$) will be less than an

4 If the risks of the insured are not independent, then the advantage of risk sharing are reduced for positively correlated risks and increased for negatively correlated risks. To see this, let α_{ij} be the correlation coefficient between the ith and jth distribution of r_i and r_j. The variance is

$$\mathrm{Var}\ (r) = \Sigma_i \sigma(r_i)^2 + 2\ \Sigma_i \Sigma_j\ \alpha_{ij}\ \sigma(r_i)\ \sigma(r_j)$$

where $\sigma(r_i)^2$ is the variance of benefits paid attributable to the insurance company's ith individual farmer's risk premium β_f^m. For an insurance company, as n becomes large, p r + A (the actuarially fair insurance premium plus administrative cost) is the smallest insurance premium that the company can offer in order to break even. As long as the insurance premium paid by the farmer, β_f, is less than β_f^m, the farmer, by purchasing insurance, can increase his (her) CE net return. In this situation, a beneficial exchange between an individual farmer and an insurance company can be achieved.

Additionally, for the farmer to have incentive to adopt BNMP τ^b, the CE net return of τ^b, r + w - β_f in Table 8.1, must be larger than the expected net return of τ^a, Max [E[$\pi(\tau^a)$]. That is, $\beta_f \leq r + w - \text{Max } E[\pi(\tau^a)]$. Combining this inequality with inequality (8.16), an actuarially sound insurance premium β_i must satisfy the following condition:

$$(8.17) \quad p\,r + A \leq \beta_i \leq r + w - \text{Max } E[\pi(\tau^a)].$$

A Decision Model for Timing Nitrogen Fertilizer Application

A field-level decision model is used to determine the CE net return (expected net return and risk cost) to a risk-averse farmer for adjusting his (her) N fertilizer application timing. This information is needed for developing a BNMP adoption insurance program. It helps an insurance company design an actuarially sound insurance program, and it enables a farmer to decide on whether to adopt a BNMP when an adoption insurance program is available. A detailed description of this model is provided in Chapter 3.

Similar to the insurance decision model, the timing decision model assumes that a farmer's decision to adopt a BNMP is based on the maximization of his (her) expected utility of net return and that the expected utility function can be approximated by the expected value-variance (EV) of net farm income. For a specific practice, τ, the objective function is approximated by (Pratt [1964] and Robison and Barry [1987])

$$(8.18) \quad CE(\tau) = E[\pi(\tau)] - \lambda/2 \, Var(\pi(\tau))$$

where

$$E[\pi(\tau)] = (1-p)\, E[\pi(\tau)]_1 + p\, E[\pi(\tau)]_2$$
$$E[\pi(\tau)]_1 = E[p_c\, Y(N_a) - F_f N_f - F_s N_s - F_g N_g - C(N_f) - C(N_s) - C(N_g)]$$
$$E[\pi(\tau)]_2 = E[p_c\, Y(N_a \mid Ng = 0) - F_f N_f - F_s N_s - C(N_f) - C(N_s)]$$
$$N_a = N_f d_f + F_s d_s + N_g$$
$$Var(\pi(\tau)) = p\,(1-p)\,(E[\pi(\tau)]_1 - E[\pi(\tau)]_2)2$$

---

policyholder. A positive value of α_{ij} increases total variance while a negative value of α_{ij} has the opposite effect.

and where p is the probability of not being able to apply N fertilizer during the growing season, Y(*) is the yield function, p_c is the price of the crop, N_f, N_s, and N_g are, respectively, nitrogen fertilizer application rates in the Fall, in the Spring, and during the growing season and F_f, F_s, and F_g are the corresponding fertilizer prices, and $C(N_f)$, $C(N_s)$, and $C(N_g)$ are the corresponding nitrogen fertilizer application costs. The factors d_f and d_s represent the corresponding percentages of N fertilizer applied in the Fall and in the Spring that are available for plant uptake during the growing season. The factor λ is an assumed absolute risk aversion coefficient equal to 0.02. This is the upper bound value for a relatively high level of risk aversion when the utility function is unknown (Boggess and Ritchie, 1988). Note that $\lambda = 0$ for a risk neutral farmer.

Maximization of the objective function (equation (8.18)) will determine the optimal application timing and the application rate of N fertilizer for a risk-averse farmer. The optimal timing can be a Fall-season-only, a Spring-season-only, or a growing-season-only N fertilizer application, or split-N fertilizer applications between any two seasons. The necessary conditions for determining the optimal application timing can be found in Huang, Uri, and Hanson [1994].

The model given in (8.18) determines the CE net return, which includes the expected net return and the risk cost for the adoption of a BNMP, for developing an insurance program. For example, if it is desirable to improve the incentive for those farmers currently applying all N fertilizer in the Spring, τ^a, to adopt a growing-season only application, τ^b, the model can be used to determine the CE net returns for the adoption of τ^a and τ^b. The CE net return for adopting τ^b is obtained by maximizing (8.18), assuming N_f and N_s are equal to zero. The expected net return for applying N fertilizer successfully during the growing season Max $E[\pi(\tau^b)]_s$ is Max $E[\pi(\tau^b)]_1$, while the expected net return for failing to apply N fertilizer during the growing season Max $E[\pi(\tau^b)]_f$ is Max $E[\pi(\tau^b)]_2$. The risk cost is $\lambda/2Var(\pi(\tau^b))$. Similarly, the CE net return for adopting τ^b is obtained by maximizing (8.18), assuming N_s and N_g are equal to zero. The CE net return is Max $E[\pi(\tau^b)]_1$ and the risk cost is zero since $p = 0$. The cost for a risk-averse farmer to switch production practices from τ^b to τ^b is the difference between the CE net returns of these two practices.

AN IOWA PILOT STUDY

Agricultural production in Iowa provides an excellent setting in which to study the promotion of the adoption of better N fertilizer application timing to improve N use efficiency. Iowa has the largest percentage of corn acres among all states growing corn receiving N fertilizer in the Fall and in the Spring before planting. Results from the

Agricultural Resource Management Study (ARMS)[5] survey for 1997 show that 20 percent of planted acres in Iowa received N fertilizer only in the Fall and about 41 percent of planted acres received N fertilizer only in the Spring, while only about 8 percent of planted acres received N fertilizer exclusively during the growing season. As noted previously, N fertilizer applied in the Fall and in the Spring is vulnerable to losses to the environment. The corn acres using Fall-only and Spring-only N fertilizer application will be targeted for the adoption of growing-season only N fertilizer application to improve N use efficiency.

The insurance and timing decision models presented earlier are used in what follows. The timing decision model estimates the adoption cost, the cost to a farmer of switching N fertilizer application timing from a Fall-season (FS)-only or a Spring-season (SS)-only application to a growing season (GS)-only application. The cost includes changes in expected net farm income and a risk cost (cost of bearing risk). Using the information generated by the N fertilizer timing decision model, the insurance decision model determines the feasible insurance premiums for the corresponding indemnities. The administrative cost and the problems associated with adverse selection, moral hazard, and the correlation of events will be ignored because the requisite information is not currently available.

(a) Data and Assumptions

To employ the N fertilizer timing decision model requires the estimation of the probability of the event that the farmer may be unable to apply N fertilizer during the growing season and the estimation of a production function. The probability of a farmer being unable to apply N fertilizer during the growing season due to adverse weather conditions is estimated by the weather simulation model developed by the Agricultural Research Service (Hanson et al. [1994]). The model provides probabilities and needed information for daily precipitation, maximum temperature, minimum temperature, and solar radiation for an multi-year horizon at a given location within the contiguous United States. Iowa is divided into three weather zones by selecting weather stations at Omaha and Sioux City to represent western Iowa, by selecting weather stations at Des Moines and Mason City to represent central Iowa, and by selecting weather stations at Dubuque, Waterloo, and Ottumwa to represent eastern Iowa. The model estimates the number of days with measurable precipitation in each of these three weather zones for the months of June and July. The model also estimates the probability of the amounts of precipitation for the raining day P (x | rain) for these two months, where x is the amount of precipitation. These two estimates indicate the probability that a farmer will not be able to apply N fertilizer during the growing season. The average of the estimated

5 In 1996, the Agricultural Resources Management Study (ARMS) survey was conducted by the U.S. Department of Agriculture. Annual data were collected on fertilizer and pesticide use, tillage systems employed, cropping sequences, whether the cropland is designated as highly erodible, and information on the use of other inputs and production practices. The survey covered corn, cotton, soybeans, wheat (winter, spring and durum), and potatoes. Only

probabilities for the three weather zones for Iowa is used in the analysis. The maximum daily precipitation that will make conditions such that it is difficult or impossible for machinery to enter the field for N fertilizer application is between 0.25 inches and 0.5 inches, depending on soil type. For Iowa as a whole, P(x > 0.25 inches) = 0.15 and P(x > 0.5 inches) = 0.10. These probabilities are used in what follows.

Production functions are estimated using the 1996 Agricultural Resource Management Study (ARMS) survey data. Sampling methods and data collection techniques used are given by Kott and Fetter [1997]. A total of 1009 corn fields were surveyed in Iowa. The data used for estimating the production function are restricted in this study so as to isolate the impact of N fertilizer applied on yield. The sample used in the estimation includes only fields that grew full season corn without manure applied or cover crops used, and planted corn the last two years without the use of N inhibitors. Under these conditions, the 1996 ARMS survey yielded 63 usable observations representing 962,000 acres. Fifty one percent of these acres applied N fertilizer during the Spring-only before planting and 9 percent applied N fertilizer only in the Fall.

(b) The Production Function

Three different functional specifications are used to ensure the estimates of the relationship between corn yield and the timing of N fertilizer application are robust. The specifications used include a quadratic function, the linear-plateau function, and the Mitscherlich-Baule function. The quadratic function exhibits diminishing marginal returns, the linear-plateau function places an upper bound asymptote on the yield response to N, and the Mitscherlich-Baule function has an asymptotic yield plateau in response to N fertilizer application (Beattie and Taylor [1985]). These three functions are specified as

(i) Quadratic Production Function

$$Y = a1 + a2\ P + a3\ K + b1(\ (N_f + N_s)\ d1 + N_g) + b2\ (\ (N_f + N_s)\ d1 + N_g\ )**2 \tag{8.19}$$

(ii) Linear-Plateau Production Function

$$Y = a2\ P + a3\ K + \mathrm{Min}\ [a1 + b1(\ (N_f + N_s)\ d1 + N_g),\ T,\ 400] \tag{8.20}$$

(iii) Mitscherlich-Baule Production Function

$$Y = a2\ P + a3\ K + c1\ [1 - \exp(-c2(a1 + (N_f + N_s)\ d1 + N_g))] \tag{8.21}$$

selected States were surveyed, but about 80 percent of the total planted acreage for the respective crops were covered.

Table 8.2. Coefficient Estimates for Quadratic, Linear-Plateau, and Mitscherlich-Baule Production Functions

	Quadratic function	Linear Plateau	Mitsch-Baule
a1 (Intercept)	83.23**[a]	84.80**	76.79[c]
a2 (Phosphate (P))	0.022	0.058	0.061
a3 (Potash (K))	-0.019	-0.046	-0.004
b1 (Linear term)	1.233**	0.940*	0.038
b2 (quadratic term)	-0.006**	na	na
d1 (% of N remained)	0.364**	0.346**	0.335*[b]
p (Plateau)	na	141.25**	139.10**
R-Squared[d]	0.213	0.247	0.164

[a] Statistically significant at the 0.05 level
[b] Statistically significant at the 0.10 level.
[c] Computed value.
[d] Coefficient of determination.

where N_f, N_s, and N_g are as previously defined. P and K are the amounts, respectively, of phosphate and potash applied and a1, a2, a3, b1, b2, c1, c2, and d1 are coefficients to be estimated.

The estimation results are shown in Table 8.2. The estimates are obtained via classical least squares. The matrix of correlation coefficients indicates that collinearity among the explanatory variables has no significant effect on the coefficient estimates for each of the production functions (Belsley, Kuh, and Welsch [1980]). The reason for grouping N_f and N_s together is that the number of usable samples for the Fall-only application is too small for the estimation to be statistically reliable. Two estimated coefficients, d1 and a1, are particularly important for the study of insurance. Coefficient d1 is used to estimate the efficiency of N fertilizer applied before planting. It represents the percentage of N fertilizer applied before planting that is available for plant uptake during the growing season. Coefficient a1, the intercept, is the corn yield if the farmer fails to apply N fertilizer. Two estimates from the quadratic production function, d1 = 0.364 and a1 = 83.23 (bu/ac), are comparable (i.e., statistically no difference at the 5 percent level) to corresponding estimates from the other two functions.[6] Note that the estimated intercept a1 (83.23 bu/ac) is relatively higher than the estimate (65 bu/ac) Voss and Shrader (1988) obtained in their study of long-term continuous corn yields without application of N fertilizer. The larger estimate from the ARMS survey data is probably attributable to a larger carry-over of N in the soil. Also, the estimate of d1 (0.364) is relatively smaller than the one estimated by Feinerman, Choi, and Johnson [1990] using EPIC simulation (Agricultural Research Service [1990]). This can be attributed to the inclusion here of data for N fertilizer application in the Fall in the estimation of the production function.

(c) Optimal Nitrogen Fertilizer Application Timing

The N fertilizer application timing decision model using the estimated quadratic production function is employed to determine the optimal N fertilizer application timing for Iowa farmers who continuously plant corn on the same field. The optimal N fertilizer application rate, optimal timing, and expected net revenue for a risk-neutral and a risk-averse farmer are presented in Table 8.3 for $p = 0.15$ and $p = 0.10$. When the probability that the farmer may fail to apply N fertilizer during the growing season is 0.15, the optimal application for a risk-neutral farmer for a growing-season-only application is 95.95 pounds per acre. This application rate is low relative to the amount of N fertilizer needed to give the optimal yield (136.82 bushels per acre). Based on the N mass balance where the amount of N applied is equal to the amount of N in the harvested yield and crop residue removed from the field, a higher application rate may be needed to sustain this yield for the long run. The relatively low N application rate simply reflects the short run condition that much of the N fertilizer needed by the crop can come from the N-rich soil in Iowa. That is, even if the farmer fails to apply N in one year, he (she) can still harvest 83.23 bushels of corn. For the risk-averse farmer, the optimal application timing is the Spring-and-growing-split season (SGPS) application. In this case 123 pounds of N fertilizer is applied in the Spring and 51 pounds during the growing season for a total of 174 pounds of N applied. This application rate can sustain the optimal yield (143.30 bu/ac) if some of the unused N remains in the soil for the next crop.

---

6 The standard error of the estimate of a1 for the quadratic function is 3.76. For the linear-plateau function and the Mitscherlich-Baule function, it is 4.71 and 3.98, respectively. The standard error of the estimate of d1 for the quadratic function is 0.118. For the linear-plateau function and the Mitscherlich-Baule function, it is 0.099 and 0.107, respectively.

Table 8.3. Optimal Application Timing, N Fertilizer Application Rate, and Expected Net Revenue for Iowa Farmers Planting Corn Continuously for p = 0.15 and p = 0.10

p = 0.15.

	Risk- Neutral Farmer	Risk-Averse Farmer
Timing	Spring-growing split	Spring-growing split
Application Rate		
Fall or Spring (lb/ac)	0.00	122.65
Growing season (lb/ac)	95.95[a]	51.30
Total (lb/ac)	95.95	173.95
Expected Yield (bu/ac)	136.82	143.30
Expected Net Revenue ($/ac)[b] (Certainty Equivalent Net Return)	316.32	307.25

p = 0.10.

	Risk- Neutral Farmer	Risk-Averse Farmer
Timing	Spring-growing split	Spring-growing split
Application Rate		
Fall or Spring (lb/ac)	0.00	92.14
Growing season (lb/ac)	95.95[a]	62.30
Total (lb/ac)	95.95	154.44
Expected Yield (bu/ac)	136.82	143.46
Expected Net Revenue ($/ac)[b] (Certainty Equivalent Net Return)	316.32	309.89

[a] The relatively low N fertilizer application rate reflects a large amount of residual N in Iowa soil. Even if the farmer in one year misses a N fertilizer application during the growing season, he (she) still can expect to harvest 83.24 bushels of corn per acre.

[b] For a risk-neutral farmer, expected net revenue = gross revenue - N fertilizer cost - field operation cost. For a risk-averse farmer, certainty equivalent net return = expected net revenue - risk premium.

When the probability that the farmer may fail to apply N fertilizer during the growing season is 0.10, the optimal N fertilizer application rate for the risk-neutral farmer is the same as when the probability is 0.15. The optimal N fertilizer application for the risk-averse farmer, however, is slightly different. As p decreases from 0.15 to 0.10, less N fertilizer is applied before and more of it is applied after planting, and the CE net return increases slightly, although the optimal application timing also involves a Spring-and-growing-split season application. In this case, 92 pounds of N fertilizer is applied in the Spring and 62 pounds during the growing season for a total of 154 pounds of N fertilizer applied. This yields 143 bushels of corn per acre. This optimal N fertilizer application rate and yield are comparable to the averages obtained from the ARMS survey.

(d) Growing-Season-Only Insurance

Next, consider an insurance program that is designed to induce risk-averse farmers to switch their N fertilizer application from the Fall-season (FS)-only or Spring-season (SS)-only to the growing-season (GS)-only. The GS-only is used to simplify the demonstration of using insurance to promote a BNMP adoption.[7] As before, let p = 0.15 and p = 0.10. As the results in Table 8.4 demonstrate, for a risk-neutral farmer, the optimal timing for N fertilizer application is GS-only. Therefore, there is no need for an insurance program. For a risk-averse farmer, when p = 0.15, a switch of N fertilizer application timing from a FS-only or a SS-only application to a GS-only application can cost the farmer $11.99/ac of CE net return ($304.17-$292.18) (Table 8.4). This result indicates that in the absence of insurance, a risk-averse farmer will not adopt a GS-only N fertilizer application. The cost mainly comes from the risk-premium ($21.11/ac). This can be reduced by an insurance program thereby potentially changing the farmer's incentive to adopt a BNMP.

Table 8.4. A Risk-Averse Farmer's CE Net Return for Spring-Only N Fertilizer Application and for Growing-Season-Only Application

p = 0.15			
	Growing-season only	Spring-season-only	Difference
Expected net income	313.29	304.17	9.12
Risk-premium	-21.1	0	-21.11
CE net return	292.18	304.17	-11.99
p = 0.10			
	Growing-season only	Spring-season-only	Difference
Expected net income	319.72	304.17	15.55
Risk-premium	-14.90	0	-14.90
CE net return	304.82	304.17	0.65

7 Another BNMP for timing N fertilizer application frequently recommended by University extension programs is to apply a small portion of the total required N fertilizer at the time of planting and the rest during the growing season. This split application was also analyzed. Note that the risk cost of a split application to farmers is less than the risk cost of a growing-season-only application in Iowa. Insurance can be valuable tool to promote the adoption of a split N fertilizer application. A detailed analysis is not included here due to length considerations. The results of this analysis, however, are available upon request.

When p = 0.10 (Table 8.4), a risk-averse farmer without insurance would have a relatively small incentive, about $0.65/ac, to switch N fertilizer application timing from FS-only or SS-only to GS-only. Since this gain is very modest, a risk-averse farmer is likely to be indifferent between FS-only and SS-only and GS-only application. In this situation insurance can help the farmer reduce his (her) risk cost ($14.90/ac) thereby increasing his (her) incentive to adopt a GS-only application.

The sustainable insurance premium for which a risk-averse farmer would be willing to pay for the coverage of full yield loss when p = 0.15 can be estimated. No administrative cost is assumed (i.e., A = 0). Assume a farmer buys insurance for full coverage of yield loss in the case of failing to apply N when he (she) switches N fertilizer application from a FS-only or a SS-only to a GS-only application. The indemnity r is computed by Max $E[\pi(\tau^b)]_s$ - Max $E[\pi(\tau^b)]_f$, which is r = [yield of successful growing-season-only N fertilizer application (146.30 bu/ac) x $2.45/bu - fertilizer used (95.95 lbs/ac) x $0.2/lb - field operation cost ($6.65/ac)] - [yield associated with failing to apply N fertilizer during the growing-only (83.23 bu/ac) x $2.45 /bu] = [$332.6/ac] -[$203.9/ac] = $128.7/ac.

The risk-free asset, w (= Max $E[\pi(\tau^b)]_f$), is $203.9/ac, which is the net return when the farmer fails to apply N fertilizer during the growing season, assuming that the farmer can harvest 83.23 bu/ac of corn in Iowa when N fertilizer application during the growing season is not possible.

Using equation (8.15) and information in Table 8.5, the maximum insurance premium that the farmer would be willingly to pay is β_f^m = 0.15 x ($128.7) + 0.01 x ($128.7)^2 x 0.15 x 0.85 = $40.42/ac. The farmer would be willing to pay the insurance premium up to $40.42/ac for an indemnity payment of $128.7/ac to maintain a CE net income of $332.2/ac. With this maximum insurance premium of $40.42/ac, however, the farmer would have no incentive to switch his (her) N fertilizer application timing from FS-only or SS-only to a GS-only application because after subtracting the insurance premium of $40.42/ac from the CE income, the CE net return to the farmer is $292.2/ac, which is less than the CE net return of $304.17/ac for a FS-only or a SS-only N fertilizer application (Table 8.4). A reduction in the insurance premium for full-yield coverage is needed to ensure that the farmer will have the requisite incentive to switch his (her) production practice.

Table 8.5. Decision Matrix for Insurance Purchase versus No Insurance for Growing-season-only N Fertilizer Application when p = 0.15

State of Nature		Probability	Choices a1 Insurance	a2 No insurance
s1	fail to apply N fertilizer during growing season	0.15	128.7+203.9 - β	203.9
s2	able to apply N fertilizer during growing season	0.85	128.7+203.9 - β_f	128.7+203.9

By implementing risk sharing among participating farmers, the insurance company can reduce the insurance premium from $40.42/ac to an actuarially sound premium of $19.30/ac (p r in inequality (8.16)), assuming that the risk for an individual farmer is independent of the risk for other farmers. This lower premium based on risk-sharing represents a savings of $21.11/ac to the farmer.[8] If this saving is added to the CE net return ($292.18/ac), there will be an increase in the farmer's CE net return to $313.29/ac, which is $9.12/ac greater than the CE net return (of $304.17/ac) of a FS-only or a SS-only application. That is, the farmer, after paying a premium of $19.30/ac for insurance, will realize an increase in CE net return of $9.12/ac. This gives the farmer an economic incentive to adopt the GS-only N fertilizer application. If an insurance company incurs some administrative cost (i.e., if A > 0), this must be reflected in the insurance premium. The administrative cost must be less than $9.12/ac and the maximum insurance premium that the insurance company can charge is $28.42/ac. (Note that this value comes from inequality (8.17)). With this premium, the farmer will be indifferent between switching N fertilizer application from a FS-only or a SS-only to a GS-only application. Thus, a sustainable insurance premium (actuarially sound to the insurance company and acceptable to the farmer) would have to be between $19.30/ac and $28.42/ac for full-yield coverage insurance to be viable.

Similar to the insurance program for p = 0.15, a sustainable insurance program also can be designed for p = 0.10 to promote the adoption of GS-only N fertilizer application. When p = 0.10, the difference in CE net return between the two production practices is $0.65/ac. Since this gain is relatively small, the farmer is likely to be indifferent between the FS-only or the SS-only N fertilizer application and the GS-only application. In this

8 This reduction ($21.11/ac) in the insurance premium also can be realized if the insurance company is risk-neutral and the company absorbs all the risk transferred from farmers.

situation, an insurance program can be used to expand a farmer's incentive to adopt a GS-only application. Using the same computation procedure as that for p = 0.15, coupled with the information in Table 8.6, the estimated range for a sustainable insurance premium for full-yield coverage is between $12.87/ac and $27.78/ac.

Table 8.6. Decision Matrix for Insurance Purchase versus No Insurance for Growing-season-only N Fertilizer Application when p = 0.10

State of Nature		Probability	Choices a1 Insurance	a2 No insurance
s1	fail to apply N fertilizer during growing season	0.10	128.7+203.9 - β	203.9
s2	able to apply N fertilizer during growing season	0.90	128.7+203.9 - β_f	128.7+203.9

where r = [yield of successful growing-season-only N fertilizer application (146.30 bu/ac) x $2.45/bu - fertilizer used (95.95 lb x $0.2/lb) - field operation cost ($6.65/ac)] - [yield of failing to apply N fertilizer during growing-season-only (83.23 bu/ac) x $2.45/bu] = [$332.6/ac] - [$203.9/ac] = $128.7/ac.

If it is desirable to reduce the insurance premium for a lower indemnity without reducing a farmer's CE net return to adopt the GS-only N fertilizer application, the insurance company can use inequality (8.17) to determine the lowest insurance premium for this reduced indemnity. The insurance company can offer an actuarially sound insurance premium of $17.69/ac for reduced insurance of $117.96/ac for p = 0.15, and of $11.14/ac for reduced insurance of $111/ac for p = 0.10. The reduced indemnities allow the insurance company to reduce the insurance premium without a reduction in the farmer's CE net return. The lower insurance premium, although not large, may increase the farmer's annual cash flow under normal weather conditions. This, in turn, may improve a farmer's incentive sufficiently so that he (she) will adopt a GS-only application.

Residual N is a good measure to use in evaluating the potential impact of N fertilizer applications attributable to agricultural production on the environment. Residual N is the amount of N applied to a field in excess of the amount of N in the harvested crop and crop residue removed from the field (Meisinger [1984] and Huang [1997]). A farmer who switches N fertilizer application timing from FS-only or SS-only to GS-only can reduce the amount of N fertilizer applied by as much as 142.60 lb/ac for p = 0.15 and by as much as 140.55 lb/ac for p = 0.10. The large savings in residual N is the result of the low application rate (95.95 lb/ac) in the GS-only application. Some of the N in the harvested grain or crop residue will be from carry-over N already in the soil.

(e) Summary of Results

Table 8.7 summarizes the results for the event that a farmer will be unable to apply N fertilizer during the growing season due to adverse weather conditions where the probability of this occurring is assumed to be p = 0.15. The case when p = 0.10 is also presented. As expected, the insurance premium becomes lower as the probability of being unable to apply N fertilizer during the growing season decreases. Also, the farmer will

Table 8.7. Maximum Insurance Premiums which a Farmer be Willing to Pay for Changing the N Fertilizer Application Timing from Spring-season-only (baseline) to Growing-season-only when p = 0.15 and p = 0.10

	p = 0.15	p = 0.10
Spring-season only CE net return ($/ac)	304.17	304.17
Growing-season only CE net return without insurance ($/ac)	292.18	304.82
Yield covered (bu/ac)	146.30	146.30
Indemnity ($/ac)	128.70	128.70
Maximum insurance premium to be paid by the farmer for the yield coverage ($/ac)	40.42 (-11.99)	27.78 (0.65)
Maximum insurance premium that a farmer is willing to pay while still having an incentive to adopt ($/ac)	28.43 (0)	28.43 (0)
Minimum insurance premium (actuarially sound premium) ($/ac)	19.30 (9.12)	12.87 (15.56)
Minimum reduced indemnity for adoption ($/ac)	117.96	111.41
The insurance premium for which a farmer is willing to pay for the reduced indemnity ($/ac)	17.96 (0)	11.14 (0)

* Figures in parentheses are the differences between the CE net return of adopting a growing-season-only N fertilizer application and the CE net return of a FS-only/SS-only (baseline) N fertilizer application.

realize a larger gain in CE net return as the probability decreases. Figures inside the parentheses are the difference between the CE net return of adopting a GS-only N fertilizer application and the CE net return of a FS-only or a SS-only N fertilizer application. For example, for p = 0.15, the economic benefit to the farmer is $9.12/ac if the farmer pays the actuarially sound premium of $19.30/ac. For p = 0.10, the benefit to the farmer increases to $15.55/ac if the farmer pays the actuarially sound premium of $12.87/ac. Other highlights of the results include:

(1) Insurance can effectively promote the adoption of N fertilizer application timing during the growing season when the farmer faces a probability of 0.15 (i.e., p = 0.15) that he (she) may not be able to apply N fertilizer during the growing season. By purchasing insurance it is possible for the farmer to increase the CE net return of growing-season only application by as much as $9.12/ac more than he (she) would realize with N fertilizer application limited to before planting.
(2) Insurance can further improve a farmer's incentive to adopt growing-season only N fertilizer application when the farmer faces a probability of 0.10 (p = 0.10) that he (she) may not be able to apply N fertilizer during the growing season. By purchasing insurance, it is possible for a farmer to increase the CE net return of a growing-season only application by as much as $14.90/ac.
(3) The range of the sustainable insurance premium for the farmer to insure full-yield coverage is $19.30 to $28.42/ac for p = 0.15 and $12.87 to $27.78/ac for p = 0.10 for adopting a growing-season only application. The indemnity payment is $128.70/ac.
(4) The sustainable insurance premium could be further reduced if the farmer insures but for a reduced indemnity. For p = 0.15, the insurance premium is $17.96/ac for the adoption of a growing-season only application. For p = 0.10, the insurance premium is $11.14/ac.
(5) The reduction in residual N can be as much as 142.60 lb/ac for p = 0.15 and as much as 142.20 lb/ac for p = 0.10 for the adoption of a growing-season only application leading to potentially substantial environmental benefits.

CONCLUSIONS

In this chapter the advantage of using insurance to help a farmer adopt a BNMP that reduces the impact of agricultural production on the environment has been analytically and empirically demonstrated. Using an expected value analysis, it has been shown that an insurance program can be structured so as to reduce a farmer's cost of bearing the adoption risk associated with changing production practices and, thus, to improve a farmer's CE net return thereby promoting the adoption of a BNMP. Using the adoption of growing-season only N fertilizer application in Iowa as a case study, it is demonstrated that insurance may be used to promote the adoption of this practice to reduce N-fertilizer use. It has been shown that it is possible for a farmer and an insurance company both to have an incentive to develop an insurance adoption program that will benefit both the farmer and the insurance company, increasing net social welfare and improving environmental quality in Iowa.

The results, however, are tentative because of data limitations and the assumptions used in the assessment. For example, the production function used is estimated based on 1996 survey data and appears to reflect the short-run yield response to the amount of N fertilizer applied. It may not be appropriate for developing a sustainable insurance program. Long run data (pooled cross section and time series data), and site-specific information, such as soil type and weather conditions, are required for the estimation of a production function for the design of such a program. Also, the estimated probability that a farmer will not be able to apply N fertilizer during the growing season is simply based on average historical precipitation data. These data may not be adequate. The probability estimation must also take into account, for example, soil type, labor availability, machinery capacity to perform field operations during the growing season, and the market supply of N fertilizer

Furthermore, the results of this chapter are likely to overestimate the cost of insurance to the farmer because the model does not consider alternative farming practices that the farmer may use to minimize the risk cost (portfolio effects). For example, a risk-averse farmer can reduce the risk cost by growing corn after soybeans (i.e., by rotating his (her) crop). Soybeans can provide a substantial amount of N to the soil for the subsequent production of corn even though the farmer fails to apply N during the growing season. A risk-averse farmer can pay a smaller insurance premium for a lower indemnity without a reduction in the CE net return. Further studies on the effects of crop diversification (rotations) and other alternative production practices on the determination of the structure of a BNMP adoption insurance program are required.

Other than the risk consideration, there are a variety of reasons for farmers not to use nutrient management practices aimed at reducing excessive N fertilizer applications. For example, some farmers prefer a Fall application to other application timing approaches because they want to have their Spring work done in the Fall to avoid possible delay in planting in the Spring. These farmers can minimize N loss in soils with a low leaching potential, by adding N inhibitors, and by applying N before planting when the temperature is below 50 degree F. Also, Fall application might be preferred because farmers want to avoid the compaction of soil caused by the operation of the heavy fertilizer spreader equipment during the growing season (Bundy [1998] and Hoeft [1998]).

There are also a variety of problems that have to be considered in designing and implementing a sustainable insurance program. For example, moral hazard[9] and adverse selection problems are often observed and well documented in crop insurance (Skees, Black, and Barnett [1997]). An insurance program for the adoption of a BNMP is likely to confront the same problems. Unlike crop insurance, the adoption insurance would require compliance in using the BNMP practices. If the insurance alters farmers' incentive to comply with application timing to reduce the N fertilizer application rate, the

9 Moral hazard refers to the fact that insurance changes the economic incentive that a farmer faces, and thus causes his (her) behavior to be different.

objective of reducing N use to protect the environment, thus, would not be realized. Some sort of mechanism to monitor the compliance is needed. If the application timing must be monitored, it can be costly and practically infeasible, causing the adoption insurance market to collapse.

Adverse selection is another potential problem that must be addressed in structuring a BNMP adoption insurance program.[10] It has been a serious problem for crop insurance (Skees, Black, and Barnett [1997]) The self-insurance problem (Bobcock [1992]) can be, particularly, a very serious problem for the adoption insurance. For some farmers with relatively small application risk they may not buy insurance. It is cheaper to apply extra N fertilizer and apply all N fertilizer before planting than to buy the adoption insurance because of the relatively low price of N fertilizer. Strategies that have been employed to mitigate the problems of moral hazard and adverse selection in crop insurance must be explored with regard to N fertilizer timing (Nelson and Loehman [1987] and Newbery and Stiglitz [1995]).

Finally, insurance can be an effective tool to promote the adoption of BNMPs. It is a market-based approach, it provides farmers with flexibility if they choose to participate, and it can be the least cost method for the public to assist farmers in the adoption of a BNMP. Further research, however, is needed because a number of issues are unresolved. For example, will it be more effective to promote the adoption of a BNMP via an insurance program rather than by the currently available voluntary incentive program (Feather and Cooper, 1995; Bosch, Cook, and Fuglie, 1995)? Will it be the least cost to farmers as well as to the insurance company to integrate the program into the current crop insurance program (e.g., the revenue insurance program) given the only option is to add a rider on an existing crop insurance policy? A separate policy may have to be designed for those farmers not currently in the crop insurance program. Alternatively, would the public continue subsidizing farmers to adopt BNMPs to protect the environment, using public funds from the EQIP? How does the public share risk with reinsurance insurance companies? What would be the optimal marketable insurance program that are equitable to the public, farmers, and reinsurance companies? To address these concerns, pilot studies in various region of the country would have to be conducted.

REFERENCES

Agricultural Research Service, *EPIC-Erosion/Productivity Impact Calculator*, Technical Bulletin Number 1768, U.S. Department of Agriculture, Temple, TX, 1990.

Ahsan, S., A. Ali, N. Kurian, "Toward a Theory of Agricultural Insurance," *American Journal of Agricultural Economics*, Vol. 64 (1982), pp. 520-29.

10 Adverse selection occurs when the insurer cannot separate better and poorer risks. The better risks find that the average premium is too high relative to their own expected costs. Accordingly, they drop out of the insurance market, which causes the premium to rise for everyone else. That, in turn, causes the best of the remaining insured to drop out, which further raises the premium, and so on until no one has insurance.

Anderson, J., J. Dillon, and B. Hardaker, *Agricultural Decision Analysis*, The Iowa State University Press, Ames, IA, 1977.

Babcock, B., "The Effects of Uncertainty on Optimal Nitrogen Applications," *Review of Agricultural Economics*, Vol. 14 (1992), pp. 271-280.

Beattie, B. and C. Taylor, *The Economics of Production*, John Wiley & Sons, Inc., New York, NY, 1985.

Belsley, D., D. Kuh, and R. Welsch, *Regression Diagnostics*, John Wiley and Sons, Inc., New York, NY, 1980.

Bosch, D., Z. Cook, and K. Fuglie, "Voluntary Versus Mandatory Agricultural Policies to Protect Water Quality: Adoption of Nitrogen Testing in Nebraska," *Review of Agricultural Economics*, Vol. 17 (1995), pp. 13-24.

Boggess, W. and J. Ritchie, "Economic and Risk Analysis of Irrigation Decisions in Humid Regions," *Journal of Production Agriculture*, Vol. 1 (1988), pp. 45-61.

Clean Water Action Plan, The National Center for Environmental Publications and Information, Cincinnati, OH, 1989.

Doster, D., *Indiana Custom Rates for Power Operated Farm Machines*, Purdue University Cooperative Extension Service, Department of Agricultural Economics, Purdue University, West Lafayette, IN, 1990.

Environmental Protection Agency, *National Survey of Pesticides in Drinking Water Wells: Phase Report*, EPA 570/9-90-015, U.S. Environmental Protection Agency, Washington, DC, 1990.

Feinerman, E., E. Choi, and S. Johnson (1990), "Uncertainty and Split Nitrogen Application in Corn Production," *American Journal of Agricultural Economics*, Vol. 4 (1990), pp. 975-984.

Feather, M., and J. Cooper, *Voluntary Incentives for Reducing Agricultural Nonpoint Source Water Pollution*, AIB-716, U.S. Department of Agriculture, Economic Research Service, Washington, DC, 1995.

Frank, M., B. Beattie, and M. Embleton, "A Comparison of Alternative Crop Response Models," *American Journal of Agricultural Economics,* Vol. 3 (1990), pp. 597-603.

Hallberg, G., "Nitrate in Groundwater in the United States," In *Nitrogen Management and Groundwater Protection*, edited by R.F. Follett, Elsevier Scientific Publishers, Amsterdam, 1989.

Hanson, C., K. Cumming, D. Woolhiser, and C. Richardson, *Microcomputer Program for Daily Weather Simulation in the Contiguous United States*, ARS-114 Agricultural Research Service, U. S. Department of Agriculture, Washington, DC, 1994.

Huang, W., "Nutrient Management," Chapter 4 in *Agricultural Resources and Environmental Indicators, 1996-1997*, Agricultural Handbook Number 712, Economic Research Service, U.S. Department of Agriculture, Washington, DC, 1997.

Huang, W., T. Hewitt, and D. Shank, "An Analysis of On-Farm Costs of Timing N Applications to Reduce N Losses," *Journal of Agricultural and Resource Economics*, Vol. 23 (1998), pp. 254-271.

Huang, W., N. Uri, and L. Hansen, *Timing Nitrogen Fertilizer Applications to Reduce Nitrogen Losses: Assessing a Farmer's Decision on Application Timing*, U.S. Department of Agriculture, Economic Research Service, Washington, DC, 1993.

Kott, P. and M. Fetter, "A Multi-Phase Sample Design to Co-ordinate Surveys and Limit Response Burden," a paper presented at the Joint Statistical Meetings of the American Statistical Association, Washington, DC, 1997.

Meisinger, J., "Evaluating Plant-Available Nitrogen in Soil-Crop Systems," *Nitrogen in Crop Production*, Soil Science Society of America, Madison, WI, 1984.

National Research Council, *Alternative Agriculture*, National Academy Press, Washington, DC, 1989.

Nelson, C. and E. Loehman, "Toward a Theory of Agricultural Insurance," *American Journal of Agricultural Economics*, Vol. 69 (1987), pp. 525-31.

Newbery, D. and J. Stiglitz, *The Theory of Commodity Price Stabilization*, Clarendon Press, Oxford, 1981

Nielsen, E. and L. Lee, *The Magnitude and Cost of Ground Water Contamination from Agricultural Chemicals: A National Perspective*, U.S. Department of Agriculture, Economic Research Service, Washington, DC, 1987

Phipps, T. and P. Crosson, "Agriculture and the Environment: An Overview," In *Agriculture and the Environment*, edited by T. Phipps, P. Crosson, and K. Price, Resources for the Future, Washington, DC, 1986.

Pratt, J., "Risk Aversion in the Small and in the Large," *Econometrica*, Vol. 32 (1964), pp. 122-136.

Robison, L. and P. Barry, *The Competitive Firm's Response to Risk*, Macmillian Publishing Company, New York, NY, 1987.

Skees, J., J. Black, and B. Barnett, "Designing and Rating an Area Yield Crop Insurance Contract," *American Journal of Agricultural Economics*, Vol. 79 (1997), pp. 430-438.

SriRamaratnam, S., D. Bessler, M. Rister, J. Matocha, and J. Novak, "Fertilization Under Uncertainty: An Analysis Based on Producer Yield Expectations," *American Journal of Agricultural Economics*, Vol. 69 (1987), pp. 349-57.

Tauer, L., "Risk Preferences of Dairy Farmers," *North Central Journal of Agricultural Economics*, Vol. 8 (1986), pp. 7-15.

Taylor, H., *1997 AREI Update 1997*, Resource Economics Division, Economic Research Service, U.S. Department of Agriculture, Washington, DC, 1997.

Voss, R. and W. Shrader, *Crop Rotation: Effect on Yields and Response to N*, Pm-905, Iowa State University Extension, Iowa State University, Ames, IA, 1988.

Wilson, P. and V. Eidman, "An Empirical Test of the Interval Approach for Estimating Risk Preference," *Western Journal of Agricultural Economics*, Vol. 8 (1983), pp. 170-182.

INDEX

F

G

I

L

M

N

W